THE POLITICS OF

Pollution

J. CLARENCE DAVIES III

THE
POLITICS OF
Pollution

PEGASUS · NEW YORK

The Politics of Pollution is part of a series,
"Studies in Contemporary American Politics,"
published by Pegasus under the General Editorship
of Richard E. Morgan, Bowdoin College

2nd Printing, June, 1970

For
Elizabeth and Eric

Contents

Introduction

ALL OF US are familiar with pollution. We have all seen the soot belching from the smokestacks in our cities, seen a stream turn foul, and seen the refuse along our streets and highways. Pollution does not discriminate; it hurts all citizens, wherever they work or live, whatever their economic status. It has become a popular political issue. Those of us who have been warning of these dangers over the years can only hope the nation will be willing to commit the money, manpower and resources necessary to do something about them.

We look toward a blighted future unless there is swift action, so it is helpful to know where we stand today. J. Clarence Davies has compiled an excellent analysis of our environmental position and a review of the politics of pollution which have put us where we are.

The difficulties in enacting the legislation we now have underscore the problems we face in moving forward from here. Powerful economic interests have pulled back at every step, claiming that pollution control will cost too much, and the Federal agencies occasionally have represented those interests before the Congress.

We would not have the Air Quality Act of 1967 had industry's arguments prevailed that there was not sufficient evidence to link health and air pollution. As we were moving to establish Federal control over automobile emissions in 1965, the Department of Health, Education and Welfare said there was no need yet for a mandatory program.

It is easy to blame pollution only on the large economic interests, but pollution is a by-product of our consumption-oriented society. Each of us must bear his share of the blame. If we want air we can breathe and water we can drink, we must ask ourselves if the extra comfort of the latest technological whim is worth the environmental price.

Mr. Davies recognizes this necessity to guard ourselves against the possible effects of new technology—to act before, not after, more scars are left on our planet and its atmosphere. His thoughts are worth quoting here:

"We must begin to weigh the costs and benefits of technological innovation, and the government must assume the responsibility for identifying new problems and dangers and for balancing the risks against the benefits. However, the Federal government is currently not organized to perform such tasks, and there must be a new way of looking at pollution problems if we are to anticipate and prevent disasters rather than investigate them after they have occurred."

Mr. Davies also traces the fragmentation of environmental responsibilities among Federal departments and the effects of inter-agency competition. One of our most urgent needs is the creation of an independent watchdog agency, uninvolved with the operating programs of the government and dedicated solely to the protection and enhancement of environmental quality. We cannot afford to vest the duty to enforce environmental standards in the very agencies involved in the development of those resources for public use. The Department of Transportation should not set pollution control standards for jet aircraft. The Atomic Energy Commission should not set water pollution control standards for nuclear power plants.

The author emphasizes that any hope for the environment rests with public commitment. The American people, especially the young, are beginning to show this kind of concern. There must be continuing pressure on the legislative and executive branches for greater commitments of resources to the solution of these problems. A concerned citizen can often be more effective in fighting pollution if he is aware of how present legislation can be used and what agencies administer it. This volume is an excellent guide.

We will turn the tide of pollution only if we successfully translate concern into action and rhetoric into financial commitment. If apathy evaporates, the roadblocks to effective control of the past need not be the roadblocks of the future.

Edmund S. Muskie

Preface

POLLUTION CONTROL has become a major issue of public policy. In this book I have tried to describe how government pollution policy is made, and to lay the ground-work for improvements in the policy process by analyzing the interests and ideas competing for dominance over pollution control.

The reader looking for vivid descriptions of impending doom will be disappointed. Many of the recent books, magazine articles, newspaper reports, and television shows on pollution have been designed more to arouse the public than to inform it. My purpose is to inform. Efforts to mobilize public opinion serve a valuable function, but attention must also be devoted to the policies for which the public is being mobilized or the resources engendered by public support will be squandered and the problems of pollution will grow still more serious.

In discussing the politics of pollution I have used an amalgam of rather orthodox political science concepts. The book is divided into three parts. The first part, "The Pollution Challenge and the Legislative Response," describes the nature of the pollution problem and the growth of interest in environmental quality. I discuss each of the major air and water pollution acts passed by Congress and the controversies surrounding them.

Part II deals with the forces which have shaped pollution policy—Congress, the Executive Branch, public opinion, interest groups, and state and local government. The role which each has played and the interaction among these different forces is analyzed.

The final section examines the major policy processes in controlling pollution—research, standard-setting, and compliance. A last chapter reviews the policy process and makes several proposals for its improvement.

My interest in pollution grew out of two years spent with the U.S. Budget Bureau as examiner for environmental and consumer protection. My government experiences are reflected in this book in that I have focused primarily on the Federal effort to control pollution, partially because I am convinced that the steps taken by Washington are crucial in determining the future of pollution control, but also because I did not have either the time or resources to do a systematic study of control programs at the state and local level. Such a study is needed, and I would be the first to admit that a complete description of the politics of pollution would require the information it would uncover. I have also focused primarily on air and water pollution, touching only briefly on such subjects as pesticides, radiation, noise, and solid waste. This limitation was necessary in order to give workable limits to a diffuse subject. However, the reader interested in any kind of pollution will, I hope, find much of relevance in these pages.

At the risk of making the task of reviewers too easy, one other limitation of this book should also be noted. Probably no policy problem is more "interdisciplinary" than pollution. The range of knowledge required to understand the many aspects of environmental quality is very great, and I make no pretense at having covered this range. I have approached the subject as a political scientist, an approach which entails an emphasis on certain questions at the expense of many others which could be asked. I believe that political science has much to contribute to the solution of pollution problems, but it provides insight into only one part of a complicated picture.

I am deeply indebted to many people who helped directly and indirectly with this book. Irving Lewis and Jim Falcon, both formerly with the Bureau of the Budget, provided the guidance and the freedom which made my experience in the

Bureau so enjoyable and educational. Professor Michael Danielson of Princeton, Al Alm of the Budget Bureau, and Vernon MacKenzie of HEW read the manuscript in its entirety. I profited greatly from their comments, even those with which I disagreed, and I am very grateful to them for their time and effort. John Mong of Pegasus served as a sympathetic and helpful editor. Anne Rogers, Reba Titus, and Priscilla Bryan all assisted nobly with the typing. My indebtedness to my wife is so great that several times I invited her to become a co-author of this study. With the wisdom for which I respect her, she declined the invitations. I therefore have no choice but to assume full responsibility for what is contained herein.

J.C.D.

Part I

THE POLLUTION CHALLENGE AND THE LEGISLATIVE RESPONSE

CHAPTER 1

What Is Pollution?

EVERYONE OPPOSES pollution, yet we find pollution everywhere. One can search the *Congressional Record* in vain for a defense of foul air or dirty water. One can similarly search in vain for a metropolitan area which does not suffer from the fumes of automobiles, from belching smokestacks, or from untreated sewage flowing into its lakes and streams. The explanation for the gap between intention and reality lies to a great extent in the realm of politics.

POLLUTION AS A POLITICAL PROBLEM

Although there are significant gaps in our scientific and technological knowledge about pollution, the technology is available now to control most of the pollutants currently considered dangerous. More economic research is needed to tell us how to clean our air and water as efficiently as possible, and technological improvements are needed to lower the cost of control measures. However, the funds to control pollution now can be made available if we want them to be. The key to unlocking the funds is for politicians at all levels of government to place a higher priority on pollution control than they do at present. If fighting pollution were considered as important as fighting a war, sufficient public money would be available to meet the problem and sufficient pressure would be placed on business and industry so that adequate investments to combat pollution would be made by the private sector.

Money is not the only element needed to achieve clean air and water. Government must set sufficiently stringent standards to achieve the level of environmental quality which people want. It must have the will and the political muscle to·see that the standards are enforced. Standard-setting and compliance, while they must take into account economic and technological factors, are heavily dependent on the political pressures applied to the government and the political power available to the pollution control agencies.

Control of pollution is unavoidably the responsibility of the government. The private market, which allocates so many of the costs and benefits in the American society, is inadequate to deal with the costs and benefits of pollution. The reason for this is that pollution is what the economists refer to as an "externality." The costs of pollution are usually not paid for by the person doing the polluting, and the benefits of controlling pollution are not gained solely or even primarily by the person who installs the control measures. If, for example, a paper mill is polluting the water, the damage done by the dirty water will be felt by the users downstream, not by the paper mill. If a power plant is polluting the air, the plant does not have to pay to use the air but the costs in terms of poor health or added cleaning bills are borne by the people who live in the area around the plant. The effect of the marketplace is to encourage pollution, because air and water tend to be free goods. But we have learned in recent years that they are not so much free goods as public goods, and that the public must take steps to protect them. The only way it can do so is through political action, and the only instrument which can attempt a proper allocation of costs and benefits is the government.

Not only is the control of pollution a political problem; the very definition of pollution hinges on politics. Pollutants are those substances which interfere with the use of air, water, or soil for socially desired purposes. If we want to use a particular part of a river for swimming, the water is "polluted" when we cannot swim in it. If we want to remain healthy, the air is "polluted" when it causes disease. Pollution cannot be defined with any scientific or mathematical finality. The definition hinges on the concept of human use, and thus, while we may be able scientifically to define what level of environmental quality is necessary for particular uses, the definition of what constitutes pollution is dependent on the public's decision as to what use it wants to make of its environment. It becomes a political decision, a voicing by the community of its concept of the public interest.

This definition of pollution is not an arbitrary construct. It is the only way in which pollution can be understood, at least from the viewpoint of the policymaker. Scientists can describe the harmful effects of a particular substance, but they transcend the bounds of science when they try to prescribe what should be the level of that substance in the environment. Only by linking scientific knowledge with a concept of the public interest can one arrive at a working definition of pollution.

Underlying much popular discussion is the idea that pollution is the artificial befouling of the pure state of the environment. This is reflected in the many appeals to return our air (or water, or soil) to its "natural state." There are two problems with such a notion. First, several major forms of pollution, and many minor forms, are not artificial but are produced by nature without human interference. Sediment in water is perhaps the best example, but pollen in the air and pollution of water by salt and algal growths are other examples of natural pollution. The natural processes which give rise to these pollutants may be retarded or accelerated by human action, but the fact remains that in a "pure state of nature" one would still have some pollution.

The second problem with the popular definition is the difficulty of defining what the "pure" state of the environment is. Nowhere does there exist a formula describing "pure" air. Scientists are still attempting to define the many constituents of the earth's atmosphere, and many of the elements found in all air are considered pollutants when they exceed some yet-to-be-determined threshold. Likewise, drinking water, under the glare of modern analytical techniques, turns out to be a highly complex liquid, with many component parts. Pure H_2O tastes "flat" to most people, because of the absence of the many other components found in all drinking sources. What is considered "pure" water for drinking purposes may be unusable for certain industrial purposes, and vice versa.

Several major attempts to set environmental quality standards have been based on the concept of desirable use. The best example is the effort by each of the fifty states to establish water quality standards under the 1965 amendments to the Water Pollution Control Act. In every case, the state standards were based on the desired use of a particular stretch of water. The reasons for proceeding in this fashion are not hard to see.

If all other things were equal almost everybody would choose to eliminate pollution, despite the difficulties of defining what this goal would entail. But all other things are clearly not equal. Society's resources are limited, and the amount of time, money, and manpower which would be needed to eliminate pollution totally is very large. Certain basic segments of the industrial economy, such as power production or the gasoline engine, might have to be changed or discarded altogether. The investments or sacrifices which would be necessary would prevent society from pursuing the many other goals it has set for itself. Thus any governmental body faced with the job of establishing and enforcing standards must weigh the costs of controlling pollution against the costs of other goals—housing, education, economic growth, and so forth. It must decide not whether pollution should be controlled, but *how much* pollution of *what kind* should be controlled *where*. To make such decisions rationally, the benefits of controlling pollution must be calculated, and this can only be done by considering the uses with which pollution interferes. Such a calculation forces one to reject pollution control as an end in itself, because the real value of pollution control lies in its contribution to the broader goals of society, such as health, recreation, aesthetics, and economic development.

At the present time, scientific knowledge of the effects of various pollutants is inadequate. But even if it were adequate, and even given consensus on certain broad conceptions of the public interest, it would be impossible to avoid making difficult decisions as to the desirable level of environmental quality. There is widespread agreement, for example, that substances which harm human health are pollutants because the maintenance of health is in the public interest. However, even with the universal application of the best possible control devices, the health of a few persons (probably those already sick in some respect) would suffer. The only way to protect the health of everyone would be to stop most industrial production. Anyone advocating the cessation of all or some production must implicitly or explicitly calculate the benefits of production against the benefits of health for some members of the society. This is a difficult calculation to make, morally and technically, but it is unavoidable.[1]

The weighing of costs and benefits arises in all governmental programs. In the starkest terms, governments make decisions all the time which they know will result in death or injury to some persons. We know that if we spent an additional amount of money on early cancer detection, for instance, we could save more lives. We know that new highways are safer than old ones, and thus each additional dollar spent on highways will save lives. And yet we do not spend billions more on cancer detection and highways because other matters are considered equally or more important. The same is true of pollution control. Resources are limited and choices must be made, even though the choices will result in injury.

As the nation becomes increasingly concerned with controlling pollution, more attention is being focused on the difficult questions of setting priorities and finding politically workable methods for accomplishing program goals. In the past these questions have usually not been considered explicitly, and programs have developed in whatever directions scarce resources, limited scientific knowledge, and the political climate would permit. The "coming of age" of pollution control programs is perhaps beginning to change the haphazard nature of program decisionmaking.

GROWTH OF INTEREST IN POLLUTION CONTROL

Underlying the post-World War II concern with all forms of pollution is the affluence of American society. The massive growth in production and in the availability of resources which has characterized the U.S. economy in the past two decades affects the problem of pollution in several ways. The increase in production has contributed to an intensification of the degree of actual pollution; the increase in the standard of living has permitted people the comparative luxury of being able to be concerned about this; and the availability of ample public and private resources has given the society sufficient funds and skilled manpower to provide the potential for dealing with the problem.

The correlation between production and degree of actual pollution is extremely high. As the number and size of plants in the nation increase, the amount of liquid, solid, and gaseous wastes produced by the industrial sector tends to increase. The pollution produced by the nonindustrial sector also increases. People have more cars and use them more frequently, thus contributing significantly to air pollution. The widespread use of such technological innovations as automatic washers, kitchen disposals, and agricultural pesticides and fertilizers add to the water pollution problem. The lessened need to reuse resources because of the society's affluence results in a large increase in the per capita trash and garbage load. When increased production is accompanied by an increase in population, as it has been in the United States, all of these trends are reinforced and the pollution problem becomes more and more serious at an accelerating rate. Urbanization also contributes greatly to the growth of the problem by concentrating pollution in particular locations.

If the United States were not an advanced industrial nation with a booming economy, it is doubtful that either the public or the government could be induced to pay much attention to pollution. Concern with pollution is a luxury in the sense that a nation or an individual who is forced to be preoccupied with obtaining sufficient food, clothing, and shelter will not have the time or inclination to worry about pollution, except in those cases where it is an obvious and imminent threat to public health. Important as the pollution problem may be, it is less important than the more obvious prerequisites for survival. On the other hand, the conditions of life in an affluent society do tend to contribute to a concern with pollution. The greater amount of leisure time enjoyed by the population leads to a greater demand for recreational resources and aesthetic satisfaction, and the higher level of education enables people to comprehend better the dangers and dynamics of pollution. The control of pollution requires considerable resources, both human and financial. It has been estimated that it will cost close to $300 billion over the next thirty years to bring air, water, and solid waste pollution in the United States down to levels now considered acceptable by the government.[2] The availability of trained personnel has been a major limiting factor on pollution control programs in this country, even though the resources devoted to control have been small compared to the need.[3] If money or manpower to control pollution were clearly not available, it is unlikely that any government would try to focus attention on the problem. Affluence allows a society to become concerned because it holds out the possibility of sufficient resources to permit action.

Once a government has taken action on pollution, the very fact that something has been done tends to create a demand for further action. The issue is given publicity and "respectability" by governmental recognition, and the public learns that something can be done to alleviate the problem. Once an official agency has been established to control pollution, that agency becomes a focal point for bringing the issue to the attention of the general public as well as of other government officials. The members of the agency have a vested interest in drawing attention to the problem. If they are successful, private interest groups will take up the call for action, and new groups will be created for the specific purpose of doing something about pollution. This public concern will in turn strengthen the hand of the governmental agency. The concern with pollution thus becomes institutionalized and the pressure to take action becomes constant. The Federal Water Pollution Control Administration and the National Air Pollution Control Administration have played this kind of role at the Federal level, and many state and local agencies have also succeeded in stimulating interest and pressure for pollution control.

One final factor contributing to the post-World War II concern with pollution has been its attractiveness as a political issue. Although many industrial groups oppose stringent control, their opposition must be indirect because one cannot gain many allies by publicly favoring dirty air or water. The cause of public health is very popular with legislators and the public, and thus the opponents of action have been on the defensive from the beginning. Also, the fact that pollution affects all citizens works in its favor. Particularly in a period when much governmental action is directed toward deprived segments of the population, a program which does something for everybody becomes highly attractive.[4]

WATER POLLUTION

The amount of money and attention being devoted in the United States today to the problem of pollution is without historical precedent. Despite the recent growth of concern, pollution is not a new phenomenon. The proper handling of waterborne sewage has been a problem of public policy at least since the time of ancient Rome. In 1273, Edward I banned the burning of sea coal in London in order to alleviate air pollution, and in 1388 Richard II forbade river pollution.[5]

However, current pollution problems differ considerably from those of medieval England, and more than edicts will be required for their solution.

Water pollution today comes primarily from three sources —domestic sewage, industrial and agricultural wastes, and natural processes. It is difficult to estimate "how much" of the pollution problem arises from each of these sources, because there is no single measure of the degree of water pollution. The standard most often used is "biochemical oxygen demand" (BOD), the amount of waterborne oxygen consumed by wastes. However, the BOD measure does not take into consideration the toxicity of the wastes to men, fish, or other forms of life. Domestic sewage today accounts for about 30 per cent of BOD, while industrial and agricultural wastes account for about 70 per cent.[6]

Domestic Sewage

Domestic sewage, although it contributes less to BOD, contains most of the bacteria and viruses which account for the disease-producing potential of water pollution. Until recent years, concern with water pollution was focused almost entirely on the health effects of polluted water. Typhoid, cholera, and other waterborne bacterial diseases were constant and serious dangers in the United States and all other countries. However, with the discovery of the bacteria-killing powers of chlorine and the widespread application of filtration and other purification processes, the first decades of the twentieth century witnessed the almost total elimination of such diseases in the United States.[7]

The virtual elimination of cholera and typhoid did not eliminate national concern with water pollution. If anything, there was an inverse correlation between the threat of waterborne disease and the efforts made to control pollution. The first stream pollution investigations by the Federal government began in 1910,[8] and in 1912 the U.S. Public Health Service (PHS) was authorized by statute to conduct investigations into pollution of navigable waters.[9] The first major PHS investigations were of pollution in the Great Lakes, the Potomac River, and the Ohio River.[10] Today, fifty years later, these three areas are still polluted and are high-priority objects of government enforcement efforts.

The construction of municipal waste treatment plants for the processing of domestic sewage has been the primary aim of water pollution control policy for the past sixty years. Before the enactment of the landmark legislation of the past few years, the most significant efforts in the pollution control battle were the New Deal public works programs, which spent millions of dollars on the construction of waste treatment works. As a result of the New Deal expenditures, combined with the reduction in economic output caused by the depression, the years 1930 to 1940 marked the first actual reduction in water pollution in this country.[11]

Waste treatment plants usually employ one of two types of purifying processes—primary treatment (removal of settling and floating solids), which eliminates 30–50 per cent of the BOD, or secondary treatment (a biological process), which eliminates 75–95 per cent of the BOD. Primary and secondary treatment remove some of the disease-carrying bacteria, and chlorination can be used after secondary treatment to eliminate the remainder of such disease agents. But neither waste treatment nor water purification, as normally practiced, are very effective against the viruses and chemicals which currently represent the most important water-related health problems.

Much remains to be learned about the transmission of virus-caused diseases, such as hepatitis, and current evidence is equivocal as to the portion of cases of viral diseases that are caused by waterborne agents. Between 1946 and 1960, for instance, out of 115,690 cases of hepatitis reported by PHS, only 417 were due to infected water.[12] The health implications of the many man-made chemicals introduced into the environment are just beginning to be explored, but there is ample evidence that consumption of pesticides, for example, is unhealthy, at least if they are consumed in sufficient quantity. What minimum quantity is sufficient to produce adverse affects is a question which has not been satisfactorily answered for pesticides or for most other chemicals.

The Federal government is conducting a large research program devoted to developing advanced waste treatment processes. These processes would go one step further in purification than the secondary treatment now used in many communities. Advanced treatment systems remove most of the nitrogen and phosphorous compounds, thereby retarding or preventing eutrophication. The Federal Water Pollution Control Administration (FWPCA) has already built pilot plants capable of converting sewage into water suitable for drinking, and several experimental advanced waste treatment plants are in operation in various parts of the country. A "closed system," whereby water in a community is continually recycled, the sewage being treated and placed back into the potable water system, is now technically possible. However, there are major psychological obstacles to such closed systems, and the current methods of advanced waste treatment are economically unfeasible except in unusual situations.

In addition to a treatment plant, any plan to prevent pollution from domestic sewage must include an adequate sewer system feeding into the plant. In 1968, about 75 per cent of the population in the United States was served by sewers. Of the population with sewers, about 60 per cent had their wastes processed through a plant providing secondary treatment; about 30 per cent were served by a plant giving only primary treatment; and the remainder dumped the wastes collected from sewers directly into the receiving waters.[13]

In many of the older communities of the nation, the existing sewer system is one of the major causes of water pollution. In these communities, the sewers which collect wastes from households and some industries are also used to collect the water from rain storms. Even a small amount of rain is usually enough to put more water in the sewer lines than can be processed by the treatment plant. When the plant becomes overloaded in this way, the amount of water that exceeds the capacity of the treatment plant is dumped directly into the receiving stream and gets no treatment at all. While much of this water is runoff from the storm, some of it is also raw sewage, since the two sources of water are combined in the sewer lines. The storm water also flushes out wastes which have accumulated in the sewer lines, thus adding significantly to the pollution load. The cost of separating all combined sewers has been estimated at $49 billion,[14] and the Federal government has undertaken a major research program to develop less expensive ways of eliminating this cause of pollution. Until it is eliminated, domestic sewage will continue to be a major source of water pollution.

Industrial and Agricultural Wastes

Industrial wastes take many forms, but generally they account for more BOD than municipal wastes and for less of the disease-carrying bacteria and viruses. Two categories of industry—primary metals, and chemical and allied products—account for more than half the waste water produced by industrial sources. Paper mills, food-processing plants, and the petroleum and coal industries are other major pollution sources.[15] The extent of agricultural pollution is not fully known, but such sources as animal feedlots or pesticide runoff from fields are major contributors; for example, the pollution load from cattle in feedlots alone is estimated to equal almost the entire sewage load from the human population in America.[16] Agricultural pollution is difficult to control because it often is not concentrated in one place and cannot readily be collected for treatment.

The major health threat from industrial wastes lies in the 500 new chemicals which are produced in this country yearly, and the many older chemicals and metals used in industrial processes. There is increasing evidence associating a number of these chemicals and metals with heart disease, cancer, and various other illnesses. There is no system for testing the effects of most of these substances on human health, nor is there adequate knowledge of how much human exposure to them comes from water pollution.

Two types of chemicals—detergents and pesticides—have been the subject of particular concern. The detergent problem came to public attention in a dramatic fashion when a number of streams in different parts of the country became covered with layers of foam several inches thick. A few communities also reported that the detergent foam was coming out of home water taps. Chemical investigation revealed that the detergents manufactured by the soap companies did not break down under the bacterial treatment given municipal wastes but retained their foaming characteristics. The manufacturers turned to the development of detergents which would respond to treatment, succeeded in producing them, and have now switched to "biodegradable" detergents. However, only the most visible problem caused by the widespread use of detergents has been solved. They continue to contribute significantly to the problem of eutrophication and to add to the chemical burden to which each of us is exposed as a member of an advanced industrial society.

Pesticides enter the water when rain or irrigation washes them from soil or vegetation where they have been applied for agricultural purposes, or when they escape or are released from factories manufacturing them. Several serious fishkills have been traced to pesticides in the water, and the effect of pesticides on man has been the subject of much controversy. Applications to manufacture new pesticides must be submitted for approval to the Department of Agriculture, and that department has developed a system whereby most of the applications are passed on to the Department of Health, Education, and Welfare for review and comment. However, the testing of the new substances is not as thorough as it might be, and recently the Department of Agriculture has been criticized by the General Accounting Office for lax enforcement of the registration laws.[17]

Pesticides and most of the other metals and chemicals do not enter the environment solely through water. Human beings are also exposed to pesticides from the air and in food. The same is true of radioactive substances, which represent an increasingly serious environmental problem as industrial and other peaceful uses of radiation become more widespread.[18] There are divergent opinions as to whether any harmful emissions enter the environment in the course of the normal operation of something like a nuclear power plant. However, even if no emissions escape during normal operations there is the possibility of an accident and there is the even more difficult problem of disposing of nuclear wastes. There is no method currently available for rendering nuclear wastes harmless— they are simply stored in containers, disposed of in the ocean, or buried deep underground. Such primitive methods will probably not prove adequate for very long.

The mining industry has contributed a particularly troublesome problem to the water pollution scene: acid mine drainage. Both active and abandoned coal mines, primarily in Appalachia, pour out large amounts of water which has mixed with sulfur-bearing minerals within the mine to form sulfuric acid. This acid can destroy almost all forms of life within the streams. It is estimated that 11,000 miles of streams presently suffer from such conditions.[19] A number of techniques are available, both to prevent the acid from forming and to treat the water once it has become polluted; but most of these techniques are still in an experimental or demonstration stage, and no Federal program to control acid mine drainage has yet been initiated.[20]

The fastest-growing problem of industrial pollution is what is known as "thermal pollution," the heating of streams caused by the discharge of water used for cooling purposes in industrial and power-generation plants. What has made the thermal pollution problem so pressing is the rapid growth of the elec-

tric power industry, together with the proposed construction
of a large number of nuclear power plants which discharge
significantly more heat into the water than conventional power
plants. By the beginning of 1969, more than 100 reactors for
nuclear plants were either in operation, under construction, or
on order, and the size of nuclear plants is increasing steadily.[21]
The Department of the Interior has estimated that by 1980
the electric power industry will require about one-sixth of the
total available fresh-water runoff in the entire nation for cooling purposes.[22] Thermal pollution can be controlled by means
of cooling towers, but such towers are quite expensive to build
and operate. According to one government forecast, utility
companies may have to spend a total of $2 billion for cooling
towers in the next five years.[23]

Several dramatic events within the past few years have
focused national attention on the problem of oil pollution. The
break-up of the giant oil tanker *Torrey Canyon* in 1967, the
grounding of the tanker *Ocean Eagle* off Puerto Rico in 1968,
and the leakage of large quantities of oil from a well off the
shore of Santa Barbara, California, in early 1969, were front-
page news items throughout the country. The major sources of
oil pollution are ships, offshore oil wells, and a variety of
onshore sources such as oil-loading facilities, storage tanks,
and even gasoline stations. The routine dumping of oil used in
operating vessels has long been a pollution problem, but a new
and much more serious hazard is posed by the great increase
in the size and number of ships used to transport oil. The
average size of oil tankers increased by more than 50 per cent
between 1955 and 1965, and the number of tankers increased
during the same period from approximately 2,500 to 3,500.[24]
An accident involving just one of the new super tankers is
enough to cause serious damage over large sections of the
nearest coast, as happened in the case of the *Torrey Canyon.*
Another new hazard is the drilling of oil wells in the ocean floor.
Such drilling is taking place at an extraordinary rate off the
coasts of the United States, with more than 1,000 new wells
being drilled each year.[25] Given our lack of knowledge of
the geological characteristics of the areas being drilled and
the inadequacy of technology to control accidental leakages,

each new well has the potential of becoming a major pollution problem.

Natural Forms of Pollution

The pervasive presence and impact of industrial society in America makes it almost impossible to talk about "purely" natural phenomena. However, two major water pollution problems, sediment and eutrophication, occur as part of natural cycles and developments. Both problems have been greatly accelerated, however, by the acts of man.

The sediment problem is caused by the presence of soil particles in water and by the accumulation of such particles on the bottom of streams, reservoirs, and lakes. Sufficient quantities of such soil particles in water render it unusable for certain purposes and also make the lake or stream less able to purify itself of other pollutants. This poses a particularly acute problem in artificially created reservoirs. Many of the dams built today will be useless in thirty or forty years because of the accumulation of silt behind them.

Silt enters water naturally by runoff from rain which carries soil particles with it and by the erosion of riverbanks. Road and housing construction and agricultural practices often result in a great increase in the amount of soil which is washed into the stream, and the construction of dams and irrigation channels further complicates the ability of streams to assimilate the load of silt.[26] Control of sediment and siltation has generally relied on dredging the silt out of the river, but this is an expensive method and is ineffective in removing the soil particles actually flowing in such heavily silted streams as the Mississippi or Potomac Rivers. The soil particles suspended in the water can be removed before the water is used, by means of filtration or other treatment processes, but this does nothing to alleviate the harmful effects of silt on the river itself. Steps can be taken to minimize the flow of silt into the river by controlling the methods used for construction and agriculture, but even the best techniques will only alleviate the problem, not solve it, in most cases.

Eutrophication is another problem with no easy solution,

in part because the process involved is one that occurs naturally. All lakes follow a process of aging, eventually filling up with silt and vegetation which consume increasing amounts of oxygen in the water until the oxygen is totally exhausted. Finally, the lake becomes swampy and disappears. This aging and eventual "death" of lakes is known as eutrophication. It is a process which is not yet fully understood by the scientists,[27] but we do know that it has been greatly accelerated by the actions of man. Although Lake Erie is not in imminent danger of becoming dry land, the eutrophication process there has been telescoped from several thousand years to a few decades by the man-made pollutants dumped into it.

The pollutants which contribute to the eutrophication process are plant nutrients, particularly nitrogen or phosphorous compounds. These nutrients feed the algae in the water until eventually the entire lake becomes a soupy green mixture because of the growth of the algae. Normal secondary waste treatment removes only part of the nutrients from wastes; thus, if the problem is to begin to be controlled, advanced waste treatment processes must be applied. Such advanced methods, which can remove 95 per cent of the nutrients, have been developed but they cost up to twice as much as secondary treatment.[28] However, even if advanced waste treatment were used on all municipal and industrial wastes flowing into a lake, the eutrophication process would only be slowed up, not halted, because of the large amount of nutrients which enter lakes from so-called "nonpoint" sources, such as land runoff. The Federal government has been experimenting with various techniques for cleansing lakes that have already begun to eutrophy, but most of these experiments are in a preliminary stage.

This brief discussion of some of the major water pollution problems does not cover all the known water pollutants, nor all of the problem areas; it does, however, describe the areas which have been of major concern to the policymakers. The water pollution control legislation which has been enacted in recent years has been primarily devoted to solving these problems and to providing resources for research into better methods of controlling them.

AIR POLLUTION

The first air pollution law in the United States was an 1881 ordinance adopted by the Chicago City Council. The council declared that "the emission of dense smoke from the smokestack of any boat or locomotive or from any chimney anywhere within the city shall be . . . a public nuisance."[29] Other municipalities followed Chicago's example, but there was little interest at the state or national level. Not much effort was put into enforcing the local laws, and they had little impact on the pollution problem.

All of the pre-World War II efforts to control air pollution were concerned exclusively with smoke, or what is now known technically as "particulate matter." The existence of other air pollutants was for all practical purposes unknown. This situation changed with the initiation of what might be considered the first modern air pollution control program in Los Angeles in 1947. The Los Angeles effort began because of public objection to the odors of a wartime industrial plant. It soon expanded into a general drive against the eye-irritating smog which plagued many Angelinos. Severe curbs were placed on oil refineries, which represented the major industry in the area, and on backyard incinerators. Then, in 1951, Dr. Arie Haagen-Smit of Cal. Tech. pinpointed the automobile as the major contributor to the Los Angeles air pollution problem. This discovery marked the beginning of the drive on the invisible odorless substances which are the major focus of air pollution control today. There is no longer any validity to the commonsense notion that if you can't see it, it's not pollution.

Three almost invisible substances—carbon monoxide, hydrocarbons, and oxides of nitrogen—derive primarily from the automobile. Together they account for 70 per cent of all air pollution in the United States, by weight.[30] Starting with the 1968 models, the Federal government has promulgated air pollution standards which must be met by manufacturers of new automobiles, but preliminary evidence indicates that the systems installed by the manufacturers are deteriorating faster than anticipated. Furthermore, the control devices actually increase the oxides of nitrogen emitted, and thus aggravate certain pollution conditions.

The growth of concern over pollution has been stirred by crises, both real and created. Rachel Carson's *Silent Spring*[31] had a catalytic effect in the area of pesticides, and the fallout from nuclear testing awakened concern about radioactive hazards. The air pollution problem was widely dramatized when, in October 1948, twenty deaths and almost 6,000 cases of illness were attributed to a prolonged smog in the industrial community of Donora, Pennsylvania.

The Donora incident was extensively investigated by the Public Health Service. In announcing the report of the investigation, the administrator of the Federal Security Agency, of which the Public Health Service was then a part, stated, "We can now say positively what couldn't be said before with scientific proof—that contamination of air in industrial areas can cause serious acute disabling diseases."[32]

However, twenty years later, there is still considerable debate about the health effects of air pollution. Dr. Ivan Bennett, Jr., testifying on behalf of the President's Office of Science and Technology, told a Senate committee in 1967: "Where is the doubt [concerning the health effects of air pollution]? The doubt stems from the fact that in no instance has the atmospheric pollution been shown to be the cause of a disease nor has a specific chemical pollutant responsible for worsening of symptoms or increased mortality been demonstrated absolutely."[33] Those stricken by air pollution, such as the people in Donora, did not suffer from some particular disease associated with the pollution but rather experienced aggravation of a previous weakness, usually due to some prior illness. It has also been virtually impossible to separate out the effect of individual pollutants, since pollution almost always involves a mixture or combination of several different pollutants. There is no dispute over the fact that air pollution is harmful—the problem lies in knowing what kind of harm is done and what specific pollutants are responsible for it.

Donora also brought to the attention of health officials a new villain among the pollutants—sulfur oxides. Sulfur oxides are produced by the burning of coal and oil, and the largest single source of sulfur pollution is the generation of electricity in power plants. The episode in Donora, as well as similar events in London, seemed to implicate both particulate matter and sulfur oxides. The health effects of sulfur oxides have still not been well documented, but the Public Health Service now considers sulfur oxides to be among the most harmful of all air pollutants. The Federal government has thus expended much effort in attempts to control sulfur pollution, but these efforts have met with limited success. Although several processes for removing sulfur from smokestacks are now being marketed by private firms,[34] the primary control technique has been to change to low-sulfur-content fuel. Changes in fuel strike at the heart of the American energy-based economy, and thus regulation of sulfur oxides has been one of the most politically sensitive subjects in the air pollution field.

Air, unlike water, cannot be centrally collected in one place and then run through some type of plant to cleanse it of pollution. This fact influences the whole nature of governmental programs for controlling air pollution, because it means that control must be done on a source-by-source basis. Thus, given the current state of technology, air pollution control is primarily a matter of enforcing regulations against individual polluters, whereas water pollution control is much more concerned with the construction of public projects.

The influence of meteorological factors on air pollution should also be noted. The amount of pollution which exists at a given place and time is highly dependent on wind and other climatic conditions. The phenomenon known as an "inversion" is of particular importance. An inversion takes place when cool air near the ground is trapped beneath a layer of warmer air. This prevents the air at ground level from rising and the pollutants in that air from dispersing. The pollutants cannot escape until the inversion is broken, and they continue to accumulate over the area, causing increasingly dangerous levels of pollution. Almost all the serious air pollution disasters and alerts have been associated with an inversion.

The inversion phenomenon is not uncommon in the United States. An inversion exists over cities on the Atlantic Coast 10 to 35 per cent of the time, and on the West Coast 35 to 40 per cent of the time.[35] Usually the inversion lasts for a few hours and then dissipates, but New York City also experiences an average of four days during each year where an inversion lasts for at least twenty-four hours.[36] It is at such times that air pollution does its maximum damage.

Less is known about the nature and control of air pollution than about water pollution. The almost uncountable number of air pollution sources and the necessity of relying heavily on action by the private sector makes the air pollution problem seem considerably less tractable than the water problem. The expenditure of the necessary billions by the Federal government could alleviate most of our major water pollution problems. It is doubtful that the same thing can be said of the air pollution problem, in part because of the need for improved control technology, but even more because so much of the necessary expenditure must come from the private sector.

It should be clear from this discussion that pollution is not a simple problem. Although many forms are due to the central difficulty of disposing of wastes created by the society, the particular source of the wastes, their specific effects on uses of the environment, and the medium in which they are disposed are all crucial factors in determining how a particular pollution problem is to be controlled. For practical purposes, there is not one pollution problem but many distinct pollution problems. This complexity is reflected in the pollution legislation which has been passed in recent years.

CHAPTER 2

Federal Pollution Control Legislation

SINCE the mid-1950's, the basic framework for pollution control has been increasingly determined by Federal legislation. However, most major legislative innovations require long periods of gestation, and pollution control has been no exception. Twenty years elapsed between the first major push for Federal water pollution control legislation and the passage of the Water Pollution Control Act in 1956. The 1948 Donora disaster brought the air pollution problem to national attention, but it took fifteen more years until passage of the first permanent control law. Neither the Congress nor the Executive moves swiftly in recognizing new problems. There must be a significant demand from powerful interest groups before important action is taken, and it takes a long time for awareness of a new problem to enter into the demands of the existing group structure.

Once the Federal government has ventured into a new field, the pace of legislation is likely to accelerate. The initial hurdle of Federal responsibility having been overcome, the search for more effective ways of accomplishing the task begins. Over the past seven or eight years, a large number of proposals designed to improve or expand pollution control have been introduced in each session of Congress, and several major proposals have become law. Innovations in water pollution legislation have generally come first, with parallel laws on air pollution following a few years later. Thus the 1956 water pollution enforcement procedures were adapted for air pollution control in 1963, and the standard-setting process contained in the 1965 Water Quality Act was included, with some modifications, in the 1967 Air Quality Act.

There is nothing inevitable about the pattern of pollution legislation. The scope and pace of Federal intervention and initiative obviously depends greatly on the nature of the administration in office. The rapid growth of Federal powers in the 1960's was due in no small part to the activist inclinations of Presidents Kennedy and Johnson. But it was due also to the growing awareness of the dimensions of the problem and to discontent with unsatisfactory progress being made in controlling pollution. The Nixon Administration has already indicated that it will submit major new bills for air and water pollution control. The problem of pollution will not go away, and it is likely that further legislation will be demanded and passed in the coming years.

WATER POLLUTION LEGISLATION: 1899–1961[1]

Until 1948, legal authority to control water pollution belonged almost exclusively to the states and localities. In almost all states jurisdiction had gradually passed from the local to the state level as it became apparent that the localities which suffered the effects of pollution were unable to control its upstream sources. By 1948, all the states had some agency responsible for pollution control, although the legal powers of such agencies varied widely.

Before passage of the first Federal legislation directed at the major sources of water pollution, two acts had been passed which dealt with aspects of the pollution problem. An 1899 law prohibited the dumping of debris in navigable waters, but it was designed to prevent impediments to navigation, not to clean up the water.[2] A 1924 Federal Oil Pollution Act prohibited oil pollution from oceangoing vessels but did not deal with the many other sources of oil pollution and was not very effective in controlling the pollution from vessels.[3]

The eager response of states and localities to the New Deal public works assistance for the construction of waste treatment plants led to efforts to make such assistance permanent and laid the groundwork for the 1948 Water Pollution Control

Act.[4] Between 1935 and 1940 numerous bills were introduced in the Congress calling for Federal financial assistance for treatment plant construction. Most of the bills also provided for Federal support for comprehensive pollution control planning, and a number of them contained provisions for Federal enforcement powers to curb pollution in interstate streams.[5]

Three of the prewar bills succeeded in passing at least one House of Congress. In 1936 Rep. Vinson of Kentucky introduced a bill containing financial assistance, planning, and enforcement provisions, which passed the House, but died in the Senate.[6] Vinson reintroduced his bill the following year;[7] it

TABLE 2-1. **Major Federal Water Pollution Control Legislation**

Date	Title*	Enforcement	Major Provisions Financial Aid	Other
1948	Water Pollution Control Act (P.L. 80-845)	Weak and cumbersome, heavily dependent on states	Loans for treatment plant construction	Temporary authority
1956	Water Pollution Control Act Amendments of 1956 (P.L. 84-660)	Conference-hearing court action process for interstate waters	Grants for treatment plant construction. $50m annual authorization	Permanent authority
1961	No title (P.L. 87-88)	Federal jurisdiction extended to navigable waters	Auth. of $80m in 1962, $90m in 1963, and $100m annually 1964–67	Research on municipal treatment. Seven field labs authorized
1965	Water Quality Act (P.L. 89-234)	Federal-state standard-setting. Streamlined enforcement process	Auth. of $150m in 1966 and 1967	Project grants for R & D on combined sewers
1966	Clean Water Restoration Act (P.L. 89-753)	Responsibility for Oil Pollution Act transferred to Secretary of the Interior	Auth. $450m in 1968, $700m in 1969, $1b in 1970, $1.25b in 1971. Federal % of costs rose to up to 55%.	Project grants for R & D on advanced waste treatment and on industrial wastes

*Despite differing titles, all legislation after 1948 actually constituted amendments to the Water Pollution Control Act.

was passed by both the House and Senate but was vetoed by the President in June 1938 because a section of the bill authorized the Surgeon General to submit requests for waste treatment projects directly to Congress, by-passing the President and the normal budget process.[8]

Following the veto of the Vinson bill, Senator Barkley, on behalf of the administration, introduced similar legislation with the financing section rewritten to conform to normal budgetary procedures.[9] Differing versions of the Barkley bill passed the House and Senate, and the conference committee was unable to resolve the differences before the close of the 76th Congress. By this time the nation began to be totally absorbed in the war effort, and all consideration of the water pollution problem was postponed for the duration of the war.

In 1948, the first major Federal water pollution control legislation was finally passed. The bill had bi-partisan backing (it was introduced in the Senate by Barkley and Taft) and administration support. The authority contained in the legislation was limited to a five-year period, but the act was extended for an additional three years in 1953.[10] In 1956, the first permanent Water Pollution Control Act became law, and in the first year of the Kennedy Administration the 1956 act was strengthened in several important respects.

For the twenty years between 1945 and 1965 controversy over water pollution legislation centered on two major areas— Federal enforcement powers and financial assistance for the construction of waste treatment plants. These two subjects occupied the bulk of the debate on the 1948, 1956, and 1961 acts, just as they had been the major subjects of controversy during the New Deal period.

The extent to which the Federal government must rely on state initiative or permission in enforcing pollution control has major implications for the balance of power in the Federal system and for the way in which the pollution program is conducted. The states have been jealous of their prerogatives, and they have been supported by many congressmen who believe in "states rights." The state officials have often been further supported by industry groups who feel that they have more influence at the state than at the Federal level.

The 1948 act established the authority of the Federal government to have some role in abating interstate water pollution, although the role was a subordinate one to that of the states. The provisions for Federal enforcement in the act were extremely cumbersome and proved to be so unworkable that the House Appropriations Committee denied fiscal 1956 funds to the Public Health Service for enforcement, on the grounds that the existing law was "almost unenforceable." [11]

After extended negotiations, the Congress in 1956 passed a revision of the enforcement provisions which eliminated many of the difficulties of the 1948 act. The new provisions represented a compromise between the Department of Health, Education, and Welfare (HEW) and the state health agencies. They provided for a conference among the interested parties; a public hearing if the conference did not result in action within six months; and then another six-month waiting period, after which the case could be taken to court. This became the basic pattern for Federal enforcement in both air and water pollution.

The 1956 act failed, however, to remove the greatest single obstacle to Federal enforcement, the necessity for getting state consent before Federal court action could be initiated. In his 1961 Message on Natural Resources, President Kennedy endorsed a bill sponsored by Rep. John Blatnik of Minnesota which eliminated the state consent provision, and also changed the scope of Federal enforcement powers by extending the Federal jurisdiction to interstate *or navigable* waters. The 1956 act limited enforcement authority to interstate waters, which were defined as waters which flow across, or form a part of, the boundaries between two or more states. Although these proposals met with some opposition, the Blatnik bill passed both Houses of Congress without major changes.

In addition to problems of enforcement, the Federal government devoted considerable effort to trying to decide on the nature and amount of financial assistance to be provided to states and localities for the construction of waste treatment plants. In January 1946, Truman had recommended a Federal program of loans and grants for the construction of waste treatment facilities. However, the following year fear of inflation produced a stringent budget and brought about a change

of administration policy. The grants section which had originally been contained in the 1948 bill was deleted, and the final
legislation authorized $22.5 million annually for construction
loans.

Throughout the Truman and Eisenhower administrations
there was opposition to any kind of financial assistance to
states and localities for treatment plants. The loan program
contained in the 1948 act was never funded. The White House
objected vehemently to a provision for $500 million over a
ten-year period in Federal waste treatment grants which was
added to the 1956 legislation. A veto was considered, but the
President signed the bill into law with a statement indicating
disapproval of the grants section.

Eisenhower's opposition to waste treatment grants was considerably strengthened in 1958 by the report of his Joint
Federal-State Action Committee.[12] After a thorough search
for Federal programs which could be turned back to the
states, the committee had succeeded in finding only two eligi-
ble programs—vocational education and waste treatment
grants. In May 1958, Eisenhower submitted draft legislation
to the Congress designed to implement the committee's recommendations. The Congress declined to take any action.

Rebuffed in his direct attempt to eliminate the waste treatment grants, the President sought to accomplish the same goal
through the budgetary process. In his January 19, 1959, budget
message he asked Congress to reduce, and, after 1960, to
eliminate financing for the program. The Democrats, however,
favored increasing the program, and they controlled the Congress by almost 2-to-1 majorities in each House. Rep. Blatnik
thus introduced a bill doubling the grant authorization to $100
million a year and extending the program for ten years.[13] The
House voted in favor of the bill by 255 to 143, the vote being
along party lines. The Republicans in the Senate were somewhat divided on the issue, and the Senate approved a slightly
amended version of the bill by a vote of 61 to 27. Eisenhower,
as expected, vetoed the legislation. An attempt in the House
to override the veto fell 22 votes short of the necessary two-
thirds majority.

Kennedy came into office sharing the dominant Democratic

view that financial assistance for waste treatment plant construction was an important and necessary function of the Federal government. The legislation he submitted in 1961 called for an increase in the authorization for the grant program and in the dollar limits on individual grants. There was no serious opposition to these proposals, the Republicans being evenly split on the issue and the Democrats overwhelmingly in favor. On July 20, 1961, the President signed the bill which authorized appropriations for waste treatment grants of $80 million in 1962, $90 million in 1963, and $100 million for each fiscal year between 1964 and 1967.

THE WATER QUALITY ACT OF 1965

In the early 1960's, Congress was still discontented with the pace of pollution control. It was felt that the states were not doing an adequate job, and that the Public Health Service, the Federal agency responsible for administering the Water Pollution Control Act, was unwilling or unable to push them into taking more action. The discontent was given legislative form by Senator Edmund Muskie, chairman of the newly created Senate Subcommittee on Air and Water Pollution.

In 1963 Muskie introduced a set of far-reaching amendments to the Water Pollution Control Act. The proposals transferred Federal administrative authority for the act from the Public Health Service to a new Federal Water Pollution Control Administration which was to be created within HEW. Federal and state enforcement was to be based on water quality standards for interstate waters, a proposal first made by the Eisenhower Administration in 1955. The standards could be established by the Secretary of HEW if the states did not, after being requested by the Secretary, establish standards which met with his approval.[14]

The bill passed the Senate by a large majority in October 1963. After almost a year of hearings and negotiations, primarily on the water quality standards provisions, it was reported favorably by the House Public Works Committee. However, the House failed to take final action before the 88th Congress adjourned. In January 1965, at the start of the 89th Congress, Muskie introduced and the Senate passed a new bill containing the same provisions as the one it had passed in the previous Congress. The House passed an amended version of the bill which contained a substitute for the Senate standards provision. It required only that the states signify their intent to set water quality standards for interstate waters. If such a letter of intent were not filed, Federal funds would be cut off.

The House and Senate versions of the bill went to a conference committee in April 1965. After five months of bargaining, a compromise was reached whereby each state would have one year from the date of enactment of the bill to file a letter of intent stating that it would establish water quality standards for its interstate waters before June 30, 1967. The standards would be subject to approval by the Secretary of HEW. If the state failed to file a letter of intent or failed to establish standards, the Secretary could establish the standards, subject to review by a hearing board. The bill as reported by the conference committee retained the provision for the creation of a Federal Water Pollution Control Administration, doubled the ceiling for individual waste treatment grants, and initiated a new demonstration program for dealing with the problem of combined storm and sanitary sewers. The conference report was approved by the House and Senate without dissent on September 21, 1965. On October 2 the legislation was signed by President Johnson, who stated: "Today, we proclaim our refusal to be strangled by the wastes of civilization. Today, we begin to be master of our environment."

THE 1966 CLEAN WATER RESTORATION ACT

When he signed the 1965 act the President also remarked, "Additional bolder legislation will be needed in the years ahead." In fact, both the Congress and the Executive Branch had already begun work on what was to become the Clean Water Restoration Act of 1966.

During the spring and summer of 1965, Muskie's subcommittee held hearings to determine the extent of need for treatment facilities. The subcommittee concluded that $6 billion in Federal funds would be needed over the next six years. In January 1966, Muskie, joined by forty-seven co-sponsors, introduced a bill authorizing a total of $6 billion for construction grants, removing the dollar ceiling on individual grants, and increasing the Federal share of the costs of construction.

The Executive Branch was prompted to submit legislation to ward off Muskie's huge proposed increase in the grant authorization. Several factors influenced the content of the administration bill. Early in 1966 the newly created Federal Water Pollution Control Administration was transferred from HEW to the Department of the Interior. The latter was much less committed to working through the states than HEW had been. Furthermore, the Democratic administration was less convinced of the value of a strong state role in pollution control than was the Congress. Thus the major thrust of the 1966 act, as developed by the administration, was to move the control of water pollution toward a regional basis, despite the fact that the 1965 act had given the states a pivotal role in standard-setting and enforcement.

The administration's proposal provided for regional agencies to be established in selected river basins. The regional agencies would have their administrative expenses paid by the Federal government, and $50 million was to be authorized in 1968 to finance waste treatment plant construction within basins which had established such agencies. The regional agencies were to draw up comprehensive plans for pollution control, and it was envisioned that they would have strong powers to set standards, enforce pollution control, and construct the necessary treatment plants.

The administration bill ran into determined opposition in the Congress, particularly from Senator Muskie. Muskie believed that the water quality standards provisions of the 1965 act represented a viable way of approaching the pollution problem. He had no intention of starting a new tack and weakening the states before the water quality standards approach had even begun to be put into effect. Accordingly, he produced a drastically rewritten version of the bill which retained some vestiges of the river basin approach but removed any real incentive to establish basin-wide agencies of the kind the administration had contemplated. The heart of the rewritten bill was Muskie's original grant proposal.

The Congress, always enthusiastic about public works programs and suspicious of regional approaches which might undermine the political base of senators and representatives, was far more receptive to the Muskie approach than to the administration bill. Congress was also reluctant to tamper with the state allocation formula contained in the existing act. In conference the construction grant authorization was scaled down to $3.55 billion over five years, and several other lesser changes were made; but the bill which passed the Congress in October of 1966 was primarily Muskie's handiwork. The administration, which had submitted the river basin program to avoid a large increase in the construction grant program, was quite unhappy with the final product. There was some discussion of a veto, but the President was anxious to salvage something in the way of pollution control legislation, and on November 3 he signed the 1966 Clean Water Restoration Act.

THE WATER QUALITY IMPROVEMENT ACT

Consideration of water pollution legislation between 1967 and 1970 focused primarily on particular pollution problems which had been dealt with only fleetingly or not at all in the 1965 and 1966 acts.

In December 1967, the Senate passed a bill dealing with oil pollution, acid mine drainage, and research on eutrophication. In July 1968, it passed a second bill covering waste treatment grant financing, vessel pollution, and thermal pollution. The House held hearings on most of these matters in the spring of 1968, but it did not take any immediate action.

The two thorniest problems were oil pollution and thermal pollution. The oil industry is one of the most powerful in the country, with many friends and protectors both within and outside the Congress.[15] The 1966 Clean Waters Act had amended the 1924 Oil Pollution Act, but the 1966 amendments contained a slight change of wording which crippled all enforcement against oil pollution. Rep. James Wright from the oil-producing state of Texas introduced in the Rivers and Harbors Subcommittee a change in the definition of "discharge" requiring that the discharge of oil had to be "grossly negligent or willful" before the government could bring suit against the polluter.[16] The amendment went unnoticed and was incorporated in the law signed by the President. Enforcement then became impossible, because of the almost insuperable difficulty of proving that the operator of a ship had been "grossly negligent or willful." The need to correct the situation created by the 1966 amendments was underscored by the dramatic sinking in March 1967 of the huge *Torrey Canyon.*[17]

The section on thermal pollution contained in the Senate-passed bill was a broad and far-reaching proposal. It was designed to meet the basic problem of no Federal agency having jurisdiction to prevent thermal pollution before it occurred. This problem was most acute for nuclear power plants, where the Atomic Energy Commission licensed the plants but claimed that it did not have authority to consider thermal pollution effects in deciding whether or not to grant a license. Muskie had held extensive hearings on the subject of thermal pollution, but the language which he put into the bill had not been considered in any of the hearings. It stated, in part, that "any Federal department or agency . . . which carries out, or issues any lease, license, or permit or enters into any contract for, any activity, shall, insofar as practicable . . . cooperate with the Secretary [of Interior] . . . to insure compliance with applicable water quality standards and the purposes of this Act."[18] This sweeping language would give the Interior Department a voice in all Federal licensing and contracts. The "Section 11" provision, as it came to be called, since it amended Section 11 of the Water Pollution Control Act, became a major focus of controversy.

The House Public Works Committee bore the full brunt of reaction to Muskie's Section 11 proposal on thermal pollution. Within the committee, Rep. William Cramer, the ranking Republican, was strongly opposed to the proposal. The electric utilities and the Chamber of Commerce lobbied vigorously to defeat Section 11. Within the Executive Branch, the Corps of Engineers made no secret of its fears that the proposal would seriously interfere with its function of licensing the dumping of dredging material from rivers and harbors. The Atomic Energy Commission was even more ardent in its opposition to Section 11. The Commission did not limit itself to defending the interests of the nuclear power industry, but acted as a spokesman for all of the electric utilities.

In the fall of 1968 the life of the 90th Congress was drawing to a close. Pressure was building up for the House to take action on water pollution legislation before the end of the session, which was scheduled for October 11. On October 3 the House Committee reported out its version of the Senate bills. The House committee bill deleted Muskie's Section 11 provision entirely; it deleted any coverage of offshore and onshore facilities from the oil pollution section of the bill; and it reduced the amount of liability for damage caused by oil discharges from vessels. Overall, the House version represented a set of significant concessions to polluting industries.

The bill was brought to the floor of the House on October 7 under suspension of the rules, which meant that debate was limited, floor amendments could not be made, and a two-thirds vote was required for passage. After brief routine debate the bill passed, 277-0. The managers of the bill decided not to seek a conference with the Senate, but rather to try to get the Senate to accept the House version.

Muskie refused to be pushed into accepting the House bill. He was particularly adamant about retention of Section 11, which he viewed as the most important part of the legislation and which Cramer, the key figure in the House, viewed as the most unacceptable provision. On October 11, the Senate passed an amended version of the House bill which restored both Section 11 and coverage of offshore oil facilities.

Adjournment of the Congress had been delayed until Monday, October 14. Both Houses desperately wanted to avoid responsibility for failure to pass the water pollution legislation. The House therefore met on the fourteenth, agreed to a series of technical amendments made by the Senate on the preceding Friday, but voted to disagree to the Section 11 and offshore provisions. Normally it takes only a few minutes for a measure approved by one House of Congress to reach the other. However, the House vote was taken at 12:55 P.M. on Monday and somehow failed to reach the Senate floor before the Senate adjourned at 2:17.[19] Each House blamed the other for the failure of the 90th Congress to take any action on water pollution control.

The urgency of passing the pending water pollution legislation in the new session of Congress was underscored by a massive oil leak from a drilling rig off the shore of Santa Barbara, California. On January 28, 1969, a Union Oil Company well located six miles offshore from Santa Barbara suffered a "blowout," and oil from the hole drilled in the ocean bottom began to spread on the water and drift toward the coast. The oil leaked at the rate of 20,000 gallons a day for several weeks, polluting beaches along twenty miles of the California shore, and the story occupied the front pages of newspapers across the nation for two or three weeks. The pressure was on Congress to take action.

During February both the Senate and House committees held hearings on the legislation, now reintroduced, which had died in the previous Congress. On March 25, the House Public Works Committee reported out a bill, HR 4148, which covered oil, vessel, thermal, and acid mine drainage pollution, and eutrophication.[20] The bill provided for penalties for oil pollution from onshore and offshore facilities, although the penalties were less severe than those contained in the Senate bill of the previous year. Thermal pollution was provided for by a rewritten version of Muskie's Section 11, based on modifications made by Muskie himself in the new bill which he submitted in the 91st Congress. This new version called for any applicant for a Federal license or permit to obtain a certificate from the appropriate state agency certifying that the activity to be carried out under the license would not violate water quality standards.

On April 17, 1969, the House passed HR 4148. In May and June Muskie's committee held further hearings on the bill. It reported out a revised version in August, which was passed with some modifications by the Senate in October. The House and Senate bills were sent to a conference committee which, as of this writing, has not yet reported out a compromise bill.

AIR POLLUTION LEGISLATION: 1955–1965[21]

The current concern with air pollution control in the United States began with the efforts of Los Angeles to control smog in the late 1940's and with the Donora incident of 1948. The 1949 report of the Public Health Service on the Donora episode had stressed the need for research on the nature of air pollution and its effects. Between 1950 and 1954 a number of resolutions calling for increased Federal research on air pollution were introduced in Congress. In 1952 one such resolution passed the House but was killed in the Senate, and in 1954 Senators Kuchel and Capehart unsuccessfully tried to add air pollution sections to the housing bill of that year.[22]

TABLE 2–2. **Major Federal Air Pollution Control Legislation**

Date	Title*	Major Provisions Enforcement	Other
1955	No title (P.L. 84-159)		Temporary authority for research, demonstrations, training
1963	Clean Air Act (P.L. 88-206)	Hearings-conference-court procedure for interstate air pollution	Permanent authority. Grants to state and local control agencies
1965	Motor Vehicle Air Pollution Control Act** (P.L. 89-272)	Federal regulation of emissions from new automobiles	Research on motor vehicle and sulfur oxides emissions
1967	Air Quality Act (P.L. 90-148)	Federal-state standard-setting for air quality control regions. Streamlined enforcement process	Registration of fuel additives. Establishment of advisory groups

*Despite differing titles, all legislation after 1963 actually constituted amendments to the Clean Air Act.
**The Motor Vehicle Act was Title II of P.L. 89-272. Title I consisted of minor amendments to the 1963 act and Title III was the Solid Waste Act.

President Eisenhower, responding to a suggestion from Kuchel and Capehart, in 1954 established an interdepartmental committee to examine what action the Federal government should take in the air pollution field. In the fall of 1954 the committee reported to the President that legislation should be passed creating a broad Federal program of research and technical assistance. Eisenhower did not submit legislation to the Congress, but in his January 1955 health message he recommended stepped-up research on air pollution. Kuchel introduced legislation authorizing a Federal program of research, training, and demonstrations. The administration did not oppose the bill and there was only minor controversy over some of the provisions in the Congress. The act was signed by the President on July 14, 1955. It authorized $5 million annually for five years to support Federal research and to give assistance to states and educational institutions in training personnel and carrying out research and control.

It took a long time for the Federal government to perceive the nature and dimensions of the air pollution problem: seven years elapsed between the time of Donora and the passage of the first legislation. At the time the 1955 act was being considered by Congress, HEW told the chairman of the Senate Public Works Committee that "instances of troublesome interstate air pollution are few in number."[23] An internal Bureau of the Budget memorandum pointed out that "unlike water pollution, air pollution . . . is essentially a local problem."[24] The Public Health Service and HEW were divided on the need for Federal enforcement authority, and Eisenhower and the Budget Bureau were definitely opposed to such authority. These views of the problem resulted in eight more years elapsing between the 1955 act and the passage of the first permanent Federal air pollution legislation.

In 1959 the 1955 act was extended for four more years.[25] In 1960 and again in 1961 the Senate passed a bill sponsored by Senator Kuchel authorizing the Surgeon General to hold hearings on particular interstate air pollution problems, but in both years the House failed to take action. In 1961, in his Special Message on Natural Resources, President Kennedy stated, "We need an effective Federal air pollution control program now."[26]

In 1962 the President asked the House to pass the bill which had already cleared the Senate, and he also submitted legislation expanding the research provisions of the existing act and providing for Federal grants to state and local air pollution control agencies for developing and initiating, or improving, programs. The House again deferred action because Rep. Roberts, chairman of the Subcommittee on Health and Safety, stated that he wanted to go into the proposals more thoroughly in the next session of Congress. The House proposed a simple two-year extension of the current authority. This was approved by the Senate and signed by the President, although the administration was clearly not satisfied with this outcome.[27]

During 1962, because of the White House request for new legislation and because of the impending expiration of the existing authority, a number of air pollution bills were introduced in both Houses of Congress and extensive negotiations took place within the Executive Branch on what role the Federal government should play in controlling air pollution. The question received added emphasis from the "Killer Smog" which hit London in December of 1962. In February 1963, President Kennedy recommended legislation

> authorizing the Public Health Service of the Department of Health, Education, and Welfare: (a) To engage in a more intensive research program . . . (b) To provide financial stimulation to states and local air pollution control agencies through project grants . . . (c) To conduct studies on air pollution problems of interstate or nationwide significance; and (d) To take action to abate interstate air pollution, along the general lines of the existing water pollution control enforcement measures.[28]

Debate in the Congress centered on the proposal for Federal enforcement powers. A bill containing the administration's provisions passed the House in July, with the Democrats voting almost unanimously in favor and a majority of Republicans opposed. In November the Senate passed an amended version of the House bill, and on December 10 both Houses approved a version of the bill produced by a conference committee. On December 17, 1963, President Johnson signed the Clean Air Act into law. The final bill squared with the recommendations which Kennedy had made at the beginning of the year. The enforcement provisions followed the pattern of the water pollution abatement procedure. At the request of a state, HEW could hold a public hearing on pollution within that state, then a conference, and finally Federal court proceedings if satisfactory action was not taken by the polluters. If the pollution originated in one state but affected persons in another, then HEW could act on its own initiative without state permission. The bill authorized $95 million over a three-year period for the air pollution program.

With the passage of the Clean Air Act, attention shifted to the problem of air pollution from automobiles. Since the 1951 discovery that automobiles were the major source of Los Angeles smog, it had been clear that auto exhausts were a prime contributor to air pollution. Research in other cities had increasingly confirmed that the Los Angeles problem was not unique but was typical of most major urban areas. The Congress in 1960 passed legislation directing the Surgeon General to make a study of the effects of motor vehicle exhaust fumes on the public health.[29]

During 1964 Muskie's Senate Subcommittee on Air and Water Pollution held hearings around the country on the air pollution problem. It became clear from the hearings that two major gaps in the existing Federal authority were the regulation of automobile emissions and steps to improve the disposal of garbage and trash. In January 1965, Muskie thus introduced a bill providing for Federal standards and enforcement for air pollution from new automobiles. The Muskie bill also contained a separate title initiating a Federal program of support to deal with the solid waste disposal problem.

HEW, having followed the Muskie hearings, presented a similar proposal for auto regulation to the White House. The President reacted negatively, preferring to see if the automobile industry would cooperate voluntarily before subjecting it to Federal enforcement. Two months after the President's reaction, James Quigley, Assistant Secretary of HEW, was called by the Senate subcommittee to testify on the Muskie bill. The Bureau of the Budget ruled that HEW was bound by the President's decision, and Quigley duly testified on April 6 that the administration opposed the major provisions of the Muskie bill. Muskie was appalled, and Quigley's April 6 testimony met with widespread denunciation in the press. *The New York Times, The Wall Street Journal, The Washington Post,* and the Los Angeles *Times* all editorialized against the administration stand. The President, realizing that a political error had been committed, reversed his position. Quigley reappeared before the subcommittee on April 9, and, stating that his previous

testimony had been "completely misunderstood," volunteered
to work with the committee to improve the language of the
bill.[30]

Following Quigley's reversal, the air pollution provisions of
the Muskie bill met with little opposition. The automobile industry did not object strongly, because it feared fifty diverse
state standards far more than a uniform Federal standard. The
industry did succeed in having the House committee weaken
some of the provisions, but the bill easily passed the Senate
and the House and was signed by the President on October
20, 1965.

The 1965 act gave the Secretary of HEW authority to establish regulations controlling emissions from all new motor
vehicles. Although no deadline was set in the law for the establishment of the regulations, HEW agreed in the hearings
that it would promulgate rules applicable to 1968 model
automobiles. The state of California had already pioneered
the way in establishing emission controls, and in fact the regulations which HEW was to apply to the 1968 models were the
same regulations which California had developed for 1967
models within the state. The 1965 act also contained several
lesser amendments to the 1963 Clean Air Act. These included
provisions for the abatement of U.S. air pollution sources
which endangered the health or welfare of persons in Canada
or Mexico, and authority for HEW to call a conference to focus
attention on potential sources of air pollution.

THE AIR QUALITY ACT OF 1967

Public pressure on the Federal government to control air
pollution increased greatly between 1963 and 1966, and there
was a widespread feeling both in Congress and the Executive
Branch that satisfactory progress was not being made. Concern
both within the government and outside it was given dramatic
focus by a November 1966 pollution episode in New York City
where a four-day inversion was estimated to have caused the
death of eighty persons.

The month after the New York episode, 4,000 people convened in Washington for the Third National Conference on
Air Pollution. HEW planned to use the conference as a spring-

board for new comprehensive air pollution legislation featuring regional control organizations and national emission standards. In his keynote address to the conference, John Gardner, the Secretary of HEW, stated, "State and local governments have been slow in seizing the opportunities for action. In particular, they have failed to establish the regional approaches demanded by a problem that ignores traditional state boundaries. . . . Another matter which you will surely want to discuss at length is the question of standards. Lack of uniform air quality and emission standards serves as a deterrent both to States and communities and to industry."[31] Muskie also addressed the conference and, while agreeing that new approaches were needed, clearly indicated his opposition to national standards. "With the exception of moving sources of pollution (for example, automobiles)," he stated, "I do not favor fixed national emission standards for individual sources of pollution."[32] The administration chose to ignore Muskie's opposition.

On January 30, 1967, President Johnson delivered a message to the Congress on "Protecting Our Natural Heritage." The message gave primary emphasis to the air pollution problem and called for major new legislation to be known as the Air Quality Act of 1967. The proposed act was to include national emission standards for major industrial sources of pollution and the establishment of regional air quality commissions to enforce pollution control measures in "regional airsheds" which cut across state and local boundaries. The President also called for Federal assistance to initiate state automobile pollution inspection systems, a major increase in the Federal air pollution research effort, and Federal registration of motor fuel additives such as tetra-ethyl lead.

Between February and May, Senator Muskie held an extensive series of hearings covering all aspects of the administration bill. Industry spokesmen were unanimous in their opposition to national emission standards, and Muskie indicated his own reservations about the proposal. The whole question of standard-setting was the subject of considerable confusion and dispute. In addition to the national standards for selected industries, the administration proposal gave authority to the regional commissions to set standards for their particular regions. The commissions were to be staffed and financed by the Federal government, and the Secretary of HEW was given complete authority to review and modify their proposed standards. Thus the bill envisioned a dominant Federal role in the establishment and enforcement of air quality standards.

A further controversy which ran throughout the hearings and which had a significant impact on consideration of the bill in Muskie's committee was the problem of sulfur oxides. Early in March HEW had made a series of decisions which put the department on record as favoring sulfur standards so stringent that industry claimed they threatened to eliminate the use of coal in the nation's largest metropolitan areas. Jennings Randolph, the chairman of the Senate Public Works Committee, came from the coal-producing state of West Virginia and was not insensitive to the interests of the coal industry. Randolph was Muskie's chairman, the air and water pollution group being a subcommittee of the Public Works Committee. Thus Randolph was in a key position to influence the legislation. During April he submitted a set of extensive amendments to the bill which, among other major changes, would have removed the air pollution program from the Public Health Service and placed it under a separate Air Quality Administration.

On July 15, Muskie reported a bill which clearly bore the committee's imprint. National emission standards were relegated to a two-year study to be conducted by HEW. The regional commissions were retained, but instead of being instruments of the Federal government their standard-setting function was made part of a process which rested heavily on state initiative. This process, developed by Muskie and clearly drawing on the precedent of the 1965 Water Quality Act, gave the states 90 days from the time HEW issued criteria for a specific pollutant to file a letter of intent stating that within 180 days they would establish standards for that pollutant, such standards to be applicable in air quality control regions which would be designated by the Secretary of HEW for each state. The Secretary of HEW would have the power to approve the state standards and to set such standards himself if a state failed to comply with the deadline. The Muskie bill passed the Senate by unanimous vote.

The House sharply reduced the large increase in appropriation authorizations contained in the Senate bill and made several other minor changes. Much of the House debate was concerned with whether California should be permitted to set more stringent emission standards on motor vehicles than the standards set by the Federal government. The Senate bill had allowed California to retain its more stringent standards, but the House Interstate and Foreign Commerce Committee, in a move prompted by Rep. Dingell of Michigan and the automobile manufacturers, had deleted the Senate language. The Dingell amendment provoked an extraordinary degree of public opposition among California residents, and the California congressional delegation succeeded in having the House Committee's decision reversed by a floor vote of 152 to 58, thus restoring the Senate language allowing California to set its own standards.

A conference committee had little difficulty in reconciling the House and Senate versions, and on November 14 the compromise version was approved by both Houses. On November 21, 1967, President Johnson signed the Air Quality Act into law.

The act the President signed was a highly complex piece of legislation, which bore the marks of the powerful forces that had helped to shape it. Many of the President's original recommendations had survived the congressional process. Assistance for state vehicle inspection, registration of fuel additives, a greatly accelerated research effort, and a regional orientation for standard-setting were all contained in the final bill. The influence of Senator Randolph had also left its mark on the bill. A separate authorization for pollution research, a requirement that HEW reconsider its criteria for sulfur oxides and that all future criteria be accompanied by recommended control techniques, the establishment of several advisory committees to HEW to ensure that industry opinion would be heard, and changes in the enforcement procedure to ensure that all concerned parties would be represented were among the contributions made by the senator from West Virginia.

The greatest contribution to the bill had come from Senator Muskie. He had shaped the standard-setting procedures so as to place direct responsibility on both the states and the Federal government. Before the states could act, HEW had to designate the regional air quality control regions and issue criteria and recommended control techniques. Furthermore, the Secretary of HEW was given the power to seek a Federal court injunction against any kind of polluter if he had reason to believe that an air pollution emergency existed in any particular city. The states were responsible for the actual setting of the standards, subject to HEW approval, and for devising and carrying out a plan for their enforcement.

It is too soon to determine how the 1967 act will work in practice. Some of its provisions will be discussed in more detail later in this book, for it is clear that the Air Quality Act will shape the nature of air pollution control in this country at least for the next several years.

Part II

THE POLICYMAKERS

CHAPTER 3

Congress and the Legislative Process

IF WE ARE to understand the political forces that contribute to the legislative process we must first understand the complex nature of the process itself. This is not an easy task, for the ways in which legislation is formulated vary widely according to the preferences and politics of particular Presidents and Congresses and according to the subject matter and nature of each particular bill. What follows is an attempt to delineate the general outlines of the legislative process, particularly as it relates to pollution control measures.

Since the early years of the Truman Administration, most major legislative proposals have been brought to the attention of the public and the Congress by being included in the President's legislative program. This program for each year is outlined in the State of the Union Message and then described in more detail in particular messages to the Congress dealing with selected policy areas such as health or natural resources. The messages are accompanied or followed by draft legislation which is usually introduced in the Congress by the relevant committee chairman in each House, or by the ranking minority member of the committee if Congress is not controlled by the President's party. The President thus sets the agenda for congressional business at the start of each session.

To say that the President sets the agenda is not to say that the content of his draft bills originates solely within the Executive Branch. As Neustadt puts it, ". . . most major measures are the product of long germination, much cross-fertilizing . . . the service of contemporary Presidents has been less creativity than crystallization; a matter less of seeking new terrain than of tracing new lines in old ground, thereby to mark the field for current cultivation."[1]

The ideas and approaches contained in presidential legislation have usually originated in discussions among interest group representatives, congressional committee staff, and members of the bureaucracy with expertise in the particular area. For example, the key draft of the 1963 Clean Air Act was produced by the lobbyist for the U.S. Conference of Mayors, a member of the General Counsel's Office of HEW, and an air pollution expert from the Public Health Service. This draft in turn was based on earlier bills which had been submitted in the Congress.[2] Several versions of a bill may have been introduced in the Congress over a period of years before the legislation finds its way into the President's program.

During the Eisenhower years the process of formulating the President's legislative program was comparatively orderly. In June, the Bureau of the Budget in the Executive Office of the President issued a call to the Executive Branch departments requesting them to submit legislative proposals for the following year along with their regular budget submissions. In September, legislative proposals were submitted by the departments to the Budget Bureau. During October and November, the agency proposals were reviewed by White House and Budget Bureau staff. The President then went over the major items, selecting those which were to be included in the legislative program. During December and early January, the White House staff devoted itself to preparation of the presidential messages while the agencies drafted the bills which would accompany the messages.

When John F. Kennedy was elected President in November of 1960, he established a set of task forces to work on legislative problems.[3] More than a dozen such groups were established, each consisting of a set of experts most of whom were not in the government, although many of them were later offered positions in the administration. Each task force sub-mitted a series of legislative proposals. At the same time that the task forces were at work, the White House staff and the Budget Bureau reviewed a lengthy list of proposals which the Bureau had compiled from agency submissions, campaign promises, and other sources.[4] In conference with the President these two sets of proposals—the task force recommenda-tions and the more customary Budget Bureau-agency compila-tion—were pieced together to form the President's 1961 legislative program.

The pattern of the Kennedy task forces became a regular part of the annual legislative process under President Johnson. Within the general task force pattern, there was considerable variation. Sometimes the task forces were established in March or April; in other years they were hastily convened in August or September. Some of the groups consisted entirely of those outside the government, some were essentially interdepartmental committees consisting exclusively of Federal bureaucrats, some were mixtures of people in and out of the government. The task forces also varied in the importance of the people assigned to them. One of the task forces on environmental quality (there was a task force devoted to the environment in almost every year of the Johnson Administration) consisted of nationally known outside figures; in several years the task force members were cabinet or subcabinet level bureaucrats; and one of the task forces was composed of "working-level" bureaucrats.[5]

The Eisenhower and Truman pattern of agency legislative submissions to the Budget Bureau was not discontinued during the Kennedy-Johnson years. The annual budget instructions still included a call to each of the departments to submit their legislative recommendations, and the departments dutifully responded by submitting their proposals. But the task force route increasingly became the dominant way by which recom-mendations entered the President's program. For those favoring particular proposals, the direct access to the White House afforded by the task force reports had an obvious advantage over the torturous process of clearance through a departmental hierarchy and then further sifting by the Bureau of the Budget.

The task force system also had obvious advantages for the

President. It allowed him to tap the knowledge and experience of the foremost experts and thinkers in the country. It provided a channel for new ideas and prevented these ideas from being watered down by compromises within the bureaucracy. Most important, it gave the President a way of keeping the legislative program his own, rather than allowing it to be captured by the agencies. Looking back on the formulation of the President's program during the Truman and Eisenhower years, Neustadt commented, "one might easily gain a sense of busy bureaucrats entangling Presidents . . . in processes expressive more of institutional concerns than presidential personality, the product rather of the office than of the men."[6] Kennedy and Johnson were both determined to avoid such entanglement. As Kennedy succinctly put it, "I simply cannot afford to have just one set of advisers."[7]

The Kennedy-Johnson method of legislative formulation also had significant disadvantages, however. The process was irregular, secretive, and often hurried. Coordination, opportunity to consult with those who must administer the program, and time to consider the proposals carefully were often lacking. The White House review of the task force proposals was usually hurried and was often conducted without the benefit of advice from persons familiar with the subject of the proposals. This lack of expert advice was a particular drawback in a comparatively new and technical field such as pollution control.

After the White House had selected the items to be included in the legislative program, it usually sent the specifications of the legislation to the relevant agency so that the agency could write a draft bill. These drafts were then sent to the Budget Bureau, and it was only at this point that consultation with other affected agencies occurred.

The adverse effects of this process can be seen in the case of the drafting of the 1967 Air Quality Act. With only two or three days to go before the legislation was due to be sent to the Hill, the Justice Department concluded that a key section of the bill, dealing with regional air pollution control commissions, was clearly unconstitutional. The section was hastily rewritten to meet the problems raised by Justice, but the revised proposal suffered from the speed with which it was drawn up and from a lack of review by those persons who were most knowledgeable about the air pollution problem.

Jurisdictional battles within the Executive Branch and resentment and confusion at the state and local level resulted from the inadequacies of the process by which the President's legislative program was formulated. Lack of coordination produced bills granting different agencies overlapping or conflicting functions, as in the case of the administration bills giving several agencies authority to make water and sewer grants. The conflict and confusion in Washington made life difficult for the state and local governments, which had to navigate their way through the channels of the Federal bureaucracy. The constant flow of new rules and new legislation added to the bewilderment at the state and local level, and made planning for the future an almost hopeless task. However, the defects of the Executive Branch process have been somewhat remedied by the Congress.

THE CONGRESSIONAL LEGISLATIVE PROCESS

The work of Congress in formulating public policy can be divided into three areas: the formulation and approval of legislation; the conducting of investigations; and the reviewing and approval of appropriations. In the pollution field the legislative function has been the most important activity of Congress. Much of the initiative for pollution control laws has come from the Congress, and the relevant congressional committees have not hesitated to rewrite draft legislation submitted to them by the Executive Branch.

Congressional consideration of legislative proposals is often aided by working under less severe time constraints than exist in the Executive Branch and by having a draft bill from which to begin work. Although presidential proposals frequently have their genesis in work by congressional committee staff or in earlier bills introduced in Congress, this has been less true in the pollution area in recent years. One effect of the reliance on task forces has been a reduction in the amount of congressional involvement in the drafting of presidential bills.

The internal organization of the Congress has been subject

to much criticism, and the reasons are easy to see in looking at a particular policy area such as pollution. In the Senate, primary responsibility for air and water pollution control legislation is located in the Subcommittee on Air and Water Pollution Control of the Public Works Committee. The subcommittee is headed by Senator Edmund Muskie. In the House, the Subcommittee on Rivers and Harbors of the Public Works Committee deals with water pollution legislation, but air pollution matters are handled by the Committee on Interstate and Foreign Commerce.

Almost every committee of the Congress seems to have some role to play in the pollution picture. In the Senate, for example, if the problem is radioactive pollution of air or water then jurisdiction is shared by the Joint Committee on Atomic Energy. If pesticides are the problem then the Agriculture Committee has responsibility. The Senate Commerce Committee has held hearings on nonpolluting automobiles, and the Senate Judiciary Committee has responsibility for approval or disapproval of interstate pollution compacts. The Committee on Interior and Insular Affairs deals with almost all of the Interior Department programs except water pollution, and is responsible for the overall management of the department and the approval of presidential nominations for the top posts within it, including the Assistant Secretary for Water Quality and Research. The management of the Department of Health, Education, and Welfare, in which the National Air Pollution Control Administration is located, is the responsibility of the Committee on Labor and Public Welfare. A similar mélange of committees could be enumerated on the House side.

The problems caused by the involvement of numerous congressional committees in pollution control legislation are accentuated by relations between the House and the Senate, which resemble the relations between two sovereign governments. Each House is jealous of its prerogatives and considers itself superior to the other. At times the rivalry manifests itself in an absence of contact and communication between the members or staffs of a committee in one House and its counterpart in the other. At times it results in elaborate legislative maneuvers such as those that took place over water pollution legislation in the closing days of the 1968 congressional session.

Another factor which promotes conflict and confusion among the pollution committees is a certain instability in the existing committee jurisdictions. The political popularity of pollution control has made involvement in the subject a valuable asset for senators and representatives. As a result, there has been an undercurrent in recent years of movements designed to take responsibility for all or part of the pollution problem away from those committees which now have jurisdiction. Senator Henry Jackson, as head of the Interior Committee, tried but failed to get jurisdiction over water pollution when the Federal Water Pollution Control Administration was transferred to the Department of the Interior. Senators Fred Harris and Harrison Williams have expressed the opinion that pollution control should become the responsibility of a new committee on urban affairs. On the House side, Rep. Emilio Daddario has used his position as chairman of the Science, Research and Development Subcommittee of the Committee on Science and Astronautics to urge that pollution be considered as a unified whole and not divided among different committees. He has wielded the fashionable concept of ecology as a weapon to rally Senator Jackson, the Interior Department, and other allies to his side in reorganizing the way in which the Congress (and the Executive Branch) deals with pollution problems.

It is unlikely that Muskie will be dislodged from his control over pollution matters in the Senate, at least in the near future. Muskie is an extraordinarily competent and intelligent individual who has gained considerable status within the Senate and, through his candidacy for the Vice-Presidency, a national following. Within the Public Works Committee he has consistently succeeded in winning the support of both the majority and the minority members for his proposals, and his ability to secure such solid support explains much of his success.

Muskie came to the Senate with some interest in pollution matters, having faced the difficulties of water pollution control while serving as Governor of Maine. He was assigned to the Public Works Committee, which had jurisdiction over the water pollution program. Public works was not one of the prestige committees, and the assignment was given to Muskie partially as a punishment for having voted against Lyndon Johnson on the controversy over the Senate cloture rule.[8] Prior to Muskie's arrival on the committee, water pollution had been the province of Senator Robert Kerr of Oklahoma; but in 1963 Kerr died. A vacuum thus had been created and Muskie stepped in to fill Kerr's place. Pat McNamara, the chairman of the Public Works Committee, decided that it also would be logical to give Muskie's subcommittee the responsibility for air pollution legislation.[9]

In the six years that Muskie has headed the Subcommittee on Air and Water Pollution he has succeeded in becoming the dominant congressional figure in pollution control. He has not hesitated to revise drastically administration proposals, and it is now a matter of some pride on the part of his subcommittee that administration bills rarely emerge from committee in the same form in which they were submitted. Muskie has had no trouble in obtaining the support of the rest of the Senate for his proposals, and the House has generally followed his lead, especially on air pollution matters.

The House Interstate and Foreign Commerce Committee, which has jurisdiction over air pollution bills, probably deals with more legislation than any other congressional committee. Its responsibilities include public health, transportation, securities and exchange regulations, and numerous other matters. Air pollution legislation constitutes a very small part of the committee's workload, and Harley Staggers, current chairman of the committee, has not shown any particular interest in the subject. His constituents have a strong stake in protecting the coal industry, but Staggers has usually been able to rely on his fellow West Virginian, Jennings Randolph, the chairman of the Senate Public Works Committee, to watch out for the interests of the coal companies.

Until 1964, Ken Roberts headed the Health and Science Subcommittee of the Interstate and Foreign Commerce Committee. Roberts was one of the leaders in promoting the early air pollution legislation and his subcommittee developed considerable expertise on pollution.[10] However, after Roberts's defeat at the polls in 1964 no member of the committee has shown similar interest, and during the past five years the House has generally acquiesced in Senate decisions on air pollution. Rep. Paul Rogers of Florida is probably now the member of the House subcommittee who is most knowledgeable about air pollution. Representing a conservative district, he has been protective of industry and has been influential in keeping down the level of appropriation authorizations.

Water pollution legislation in the House is the responsibility of the Rivers and Harbors Subcommittee of the Public Works Committee, which, since 1955, has been headed by John A. Blatnik of Minnesota. Blatnik, a liberal Democrat, was the prime mover behind the 1956 and 1961 water pollution acts. However, in recent years he has been somewhat overshadowed by Muskie in the Senate.

The relationship between the House and Senate Public Works Committees with respect to water pollution demonstrates the vital role played by individuals in shaping the orientation of a committee. At least until 1963, while Robert Kerr was head of the Senate committee, Blatnik took the lead in the formulation of water pollution legislation. Kerr was not fully convinced of the need for such legislation, and Blatnik played the role of the liberal initiator, fighting the Senate forces of conservatism. As illustrated by the battles over water pollution during 1967 and 1968, the roles have now been reversed. Kerr has been replaced by Muskie, and the Senate committee is now the initiating force. The House committee has become a conservative force, protecting the interests of key industries and arguing for smaller expenditures for pollution controls. William Cramer, the ranking Republican on the Rivers and Harbors Committee and a conservative, has become more the spokesman for the committee than Blatnik. Cramer's position has been enhanced by the power of the conservative coalition in the House, and Blatnik has lost some degree of power because of a weakening of his lines of contact with the water pollution agency in the Executive Branch. Muskie has thus become the leading voice in water pollution, as well as air pollution.

The Congress has generally taken more initiative than the Executive Branch in pollution legislation. It has anticipated problems sooner, been more sensitive to public opinion, and improved the quality of the legislation sent to it by the White

House. It would seem that the greater openness of the Congress to political pressures at least has the advantage of allowing the House and Senate to adjust more rapidly than the bureaucracy to changes in a field developing as swiftly as that of pollution.

CONGRESSIONAL INVESTIGATIONS

There have been few congressional investigations of pollution control directed at uncovering specific instances of wrongdoing or inefficiency. Rep. Henry Reuss, in his capacity as chairman of the Research and Technical Programs Subcommittee of the House Government Operations Committee, did conduct a one-day hearing in September 1968 on Federal air pollution research for controlling sulfur oxides.[11] Reuss has subsequently issued a report on sulfur research, but this has been the only congressional effort directed at exploring a specific situation to discover whether the Executive Branch has been guilty of inefficiency.

Reuss's investigation was typical in one respect. Like other congressional forays into pollution, it was prompted by a concern with interagency battles and jurisdictional confusion. The multitude of executive agencies and the uncertainty as to what kind of problem pollution is (urban, ecological, health, recreation, etc.) constitute an open invitation to congressional committees to investigate pollution in an attempt to create more order and a better definition of the problem. The popularity of pollution control provides an added incentive for a congressman to become involved in the area. In the Senate the temptation to probe pollution has been reduced by the strength and prestige of the Muskie subcommittee. On the House side there has been more opportunity to probe.

The major effort to create a new approach to pollution control has been that of Rep. Emilio Daddario's Subcommittee on Science, Research, and Development of the House Committee on Science and Astronautics. Daddario turned to the subject of pollution in 1965, and since 1966 his committee has held several hearings and produced two reports on technology and environmental quality.[12] The basic theme of Daddario's work has been to emphasize that pollution is an ecological problem and that it must be viewed as a whole, not just in segments. In his 1968 report, Daddario drew the organizational implications of this approach. "The Department of the Interior should be designated as the lead agency in coordinating environmental engineering operations of all Federal programs," concluded the report. "An 'Environmental Cabinet' should be formed of the designated officials from each agency. . . . This group, under the leadership of the Secretary of the Department of the Interior, should assure conformity of Federal operations with the national policy for the environment." [13]

The approach and conclusions of Daddario were quite congenial to the interests of Senator Jackson, the chairman of the Senate Interior and Insular Affairs Committee. An alliance between Daddario and Jackson was cemented in October 1968 with the issuance of a "Congressional White Paper on a National Policy for the Environment," produced jointly by the Senate Interior Committee and the House Committee on Science and Astronautics. [14] The White Paper suggested the creation of a joint congressional committee on environmental management. This followed logically from the Daddario view of the pollution problem, but it also served as a counterproposal to the idea of a Select Senate Committee on Technology and the Human Environment which Muskie, in his role as chairman of the Subcommittee on Intergovernmental Relations, had been pushing for several years.

In February 1969, Jackson introduced a bill authorizing the Secretary of the Interior to conduct ecological research and establishing a three-man Council on Environmental Quality in the Executive Office of the President. The Council's responsibilities included reviewing activities carried out by Federal agencies and reporting at least once a year to the President on "the state and condition of the environment." In July 1969, the Senate passed a slightly changed version of Jackson's bill, and an amended version passed the House in September. [15]

In June 1969, Muskie introduced the Environmental Quality Improvement Act of 1969. The act provided for: (1) The development of criteria and standards to assure the protection and enhancement of environmental quality in all Federal and federally assisted public works projects and programs; (2) the coordination of all Federal research programs to increase knowledge of the interrelationship between man and his environment; and (3) the creation of an Office of Environmental Quality and appropriate staff in the Executive Office of the President. Muskie, in his statement introducing the bill, noted that "The proposed legislation is consistent with other Congressional proposals directed toward implementing the National policy for the environment."[16] The Muskie bill was later incorporated as a separate title of the pending water pollution legislation.

The Senate was thus faced with two bills, each calling for a different approach to coordinating the government's environmental quality efforts. An extensive series of negotiations between Muskie and Jackson took place prior to Senate consideration of the water pollution amendments, and a compromise —calling for the creation of both Muskie's Office of Environmental Quality and Jackson's Council on Environmental Quality —was agreed to. The issue of committee jurisdiction was effectively skirted. In October 1969 the Senate unanimously passed the amendments to the Water Pollution Control Act, including a version of the Muskie Office of Environmental Quality proposal revised to take account of his compromise with Jackson.[17] On January 1, 1970, President Nixon signed the Jackson bill, and in February he appointed Russell Train as the first chairman of the new council. As of February 1970, Muskie's bill was still being considered by a conference committee.

The efforts of Jackson and Daddario are, in part, a power play directed against HEW and Muskie in favor of the Interior Department and a new alignment of congressional committee jurisdictions. The substantive importance of these efforts should not, however, be underestimated. The organization of the Executive Branch for dealing with pollution is confused, as we shall see in Chapter 5. The question of the degree to which pollution is a single united problem is an important one, with major consequences for public policy. The organization of the Congress with respect to pollution is not only inconsistent between the Senate and House, but within each House is as fragmented as the Executive Branch. The steps taken by Jackson and Daddario represent that inextricable mixing of personal power and substantive policy considerations which provides much of the dynamic motivation for movement within the political system.

THE CONGRESSIONAL APPROPRIATIONS PROCESS

The primary effect of appropriations committee action on the air and water pollution programs has been to approve the steady and sometimes dramatic increase in funds recommended by the Executive Branch. Changes in the President's budget requests made by the committees usually have been marginal. An examination of the air and water pollution budgets over the past fifteen years reveals that Congress has slightly increased the President's requests about half the time and slightly reduced them the other half.[18] The willingness of the appropriations committees to support the growth in the air and water pollution budgets is an indicator of the public and interest group support for pollution control.[19]

The chairmen of the relevant appropriations subcommittees are also responsible for the growth in pollution budgets. For many years the chairman of the House Appropriations Subcommittee having jurisdiction over pollution was John Fogarty. As Fenno has noted, "Among the many subcommittee chairmen of the period, John Fogarty has been the one least touched by the Committee's goals of budget-cutting. His disposition [has been] to loosen rather than tighten the purse strings . . ."[20] Fogarty's expansionist views were consistent with the requests emerging from the Executive Branch. Lister Hill, the chairman of the Senate HEW Appropriations Subcommittee, generally supported Fogarty's recommendations.

In the last two or three years there have been major changes in the congressional review process of air and water pollution budgets. Until 1967, both the air and water budgets were the responsibility of the HEW appropriations subcommittees. In 1967, following the transfer of FWPCA to the Department of the Interior, jurisdiction over the water pollution budget was given to the subcommittees on public works. The House Public Works Subcommittee is headed by Michael Kirwan of Ohio, and the Senate subcommittee is chaired by Allen Ellender of Louisiana. The air pollution budget remained under the health subcommittees, but both the House and Senate health subcommittees underwent a change in leadership. In January 1967 Fogarty died, and was succeeded by Dan Flood of Pennsylvania. In 1968 Lister Hill retired, and was succeeded by Warren Magnuson of Washington.

TABLE 3–1.
Authorization and Appropriations for Waste Treatment Grants

Fiscal Year	1960	1961	1962	1963	1964	1965	1966	1967	1968	1969	1970
Auth. (in $m)	50	50	80	90	100	100	150	150	450	700	1,000
Approp. (in $m)	46.8	46.1	80.1	90	90	90	121	150	203	214	800
% Approp. of Auth.	93	92	101	100	90	90	81	100	45	31	80

The changes in committee jurisdiction and committee chairmanship have generally resulted in a somewhat more difficult time for pollution control budgets. The public works subcommittees have reduced FWPCA requests more than the health subcommittees ever did, but it is hard to separate the effect of the change in committees from the general congressional pressure for economy which has prevailed over the past two years. Flood's views of the functions of the House HEW Appropriations Subcommittee are much more orthodox than Fogarty's were, and the air pollution budget has been subjected to closer scrutiny than in the past.

The more critical congressional review of the pollution budgets should not obscure the point that, if measured in terms of dollar reductions in agency budgets, the Bureau of the Budget in the Executive Office of the President is a more influential budgetary force than the congressional appropriations committees. The Budget Bureau in its consideration of funds for air and water pollution control is not subject to the same degree of public pressure as is the Congress, and it has therefore felt more at liberty to reduce agency requests.

The influence of public pressure was demonstrated in the fall of 1969 by an extraordinary reversal of the trend toward more stringent review of pollution budgets. President Nixon had supported the Johnson Administration's budget request of $214 million in fiscal 1970 for waste treatment plant construction grants, the same level of funding as in 1969. Under intense pressure from a "Citizens' Crusade for Clean Water," 222 members of the House (including at least 38 Republicans) signed a petition calling for an appropriation of $1 billion, the full authorized amount. The House Appropriations Committee, responding to the same pressures, sent to the full House a recommendation of $600 million, almost three times the administration request. The White House announced that it was willing to compromise and agree to $750 million, but the proponents of the $1 billion figure, operating on the same faulty intelligence as the White House, rejected the compromise. When the vote came on the House floor, an amendment calling for the full $1 billion was defeated, 148–146, and the House approved the committee's recommendation of $600 million.[21] The Senate voted the full $1 billion, and the conference committee compromised on a final appropriation of $800 million.

The change in committee jurisdiction for the water pollution budget points up the same problem as the Daddario investigations, namely, what is the proper context in which to consider the issue of pollution control? Requests for funds for water pollution control are now weighed against requests for dams, harbor dredging, and other public works projects, whereas funds for air pollution control are considered in the context of other health programs. Frederic Cleaveland, in a study devoted to congressional legislation on urban problems, discovered a different aspect of the context problem with pollution legislation. He reported that, "While Jennings in his case study concluded that water pollution was not considered essentially an urban problem, Ripley observed that 'everyone who was concerned about air pollution, both in Congress and in the executive, made it clear that the problem was centrally urban in character.' Obviously, two quite different issue contexts were present." [22]

Cleaveland defines issue context as "the way members of Congress perceive a policy that comes before them, how they consciously or unconsciously classify it for study and analysis, what specified policy setting or group of policies they believe it is related to. These frames of reference go a long way toward providing a structure to guide consideration of the proposal in the legislative process."[23] The concept is applicable to processes other than formulating legislation (the budget process, for example) and to actors other than those in the Congress. It is one of the major underlying issues in the politics of pollution control.

The context in which pollution control is considered determines (and is partially determined by) which executive agencies will carry out the pollution program, which congressional committees will have jurisdiction over the program, and which interest groups will have the most influence over the scope and direction of the program. At the present time there is no consensus on how to view pollution control, and there will be many battles before the issue is resolved.[24]

The problem of issue context reinforces the wide dispersion of power brought about by the pluralistic political system. The President can attempt to bring some degree of centralization to the process of legislative formulation in the Executive Branch, but only at the cost of lowering the quality of the bills sent to the Hill. When the bills are considered by the Congress they are exposed to the many conflicting pressures of rival committees, differing legislative constituencies, and competing interest groups. A strong leader such as Muskie can serve as the central focus for such pressures and can exercise considerable influence on the final form of the legislation, but he must frequently defend his position against attempts to disperse his power, and he must constantly operate within the parameters set by the relevant political forces. The most important of these forces are public opinion and interest groups.

CHAPTER 4

Public Opinion and Interest Groups

THERE IS widespread agreement that the state of public opinion is one of the crucial factors in the campaign for cleaner air and water. In any society, the attitudes held by the general public form the ultimate parameters of governmental action. As Ido de Groot states, "After all, it is these attitudes, be they expressed as perceptions, opinions, beliefs, hopes, desires, wishes, or feelings, that, stably and in change, ultimately accrue into political decisionmaking and socially imposed ordered change. These collective societal attitudes . . . dictate what is feasible and necessary in society."[1]

In some situations the voting public may be the actual decisionmakers, and in such cases public opinion is obviously of crucial importance. The most common situations of this type are referenda on local or state bond issues for the construction of waste treatment plants and other water pollution control facilities. Water pollution control usually demands significant capital investments, and in most localities public approval is a requirement for such investments. If public opinion has not been educated to realize the need for pollution control, the control effort is doomed to failure.

Public opinion may also be considered an important factor in weighing the costs and benefits of pollution control. Decisions about pollution will inevitably be made in the political arena where public opinion weighs heavily, but even for the person who attempts to evaluate control decisions apart from political factors, people's opinions are an important consideration. The fact that people worry about pollution is a significant cost of pollution. Public opinion may also be the most reliable available indicator of the aesthetic and recreational costs of pollution.

We shall look at public opinion and the political process in terms of three stages—"wants," "demands," and "decisions."[2] A "want" in this context is some perceived dissatisfaction potentially within the sphere of governmental remedy. The perception of such wants does not in most cases lead to any political action. A "demand" occurs when a want is translated into a request or demand that the government take action to alleviate the problem. Thus a housewife may be annoyed by the soot which collects on her windowsill each morning. If she rests content with a few grumbles and the use of some soap she possesses a want. But if she writes her congressman or joins a citizen's group in an attempt to eliminate the cause of the soot, she has translated her want into a demand. The third stage in the public opinion process is the "decision" stage, which is the action or lack thereof taken by the government.

WANTS

Public concern over both air and water pollution has been rising rapidly. About half the people in the United States today consider pollution to be a problem. The increase in this concern is shown in the polls conducted by the Opinion Research Corporation (ORC). For the past four years ORC has asked a nationwide sample, "Compared to other parts of the country, how serious, in your opinion, do you think the problem of water (air) pollution is in this area—very serious, somewhat serious, or not serious?" Whereas in 1965 only 13 per cent of the population thought that water pollution was a very serious problem, 27 per cent thought so in 1968.[3] The corresponding figure for air pollution rose from 10 per cent to 25 per cent.[4]

The percentage of the population concerned about the pollution problem ranks it as one of the major worries of the general public. Responses to questions asking people to rank pollution in comparison to other problems have varied widely,

TABLE 4-1. **Public Opinion of Seriousness of Water Pollution Problem**

| | Percentage of Population | | | |
	1965	1966	1967	1968
Very Serious	13	19	24	27
Somewhat Serious	22	30	28	31
Not Serious or No Opinion	65	51	48	42
	100	100	100	100
(n)	(1,077)	(2,308)	(1,047)	(2,079)

Source: Opinion Research Corporation, "Public Opinion Index" (Princeton, N.J., 1966, 1967, 1968, 1969).

TABLE 4-2. **Public Opinion of Seriousness of Air Pollution Problem**

| | Percentage of Population | | | |
	1965	1966	1967	1968
Very Serious	10	19	27	25
Somewhat Serious	18	29	26	30
Not Serious or No Opinion	72	52	47	45
	100	100	100	100
(n)	(1,051)	(2,033)	(1,047)	(2,079)

Source: Opinion Research Corporation, "Public Opinion Index" (Princeton, N.J., 1966, 1967, 1968, 1969).

depending on when the question was asked, how it was phrased, and what kind of sample was questioned. In several studies of local areas, unemployment and juvenile delinquency outranked air pollution as a perceived community problem, but pollution was still considered one of the half dozen most serious problems.[5] In a study of St. Louis, except for the central city area, air pollution outweighed problems associated with race.[6]

The major determinant of public concern with air pollution is the actual level of pollution prevalent in the area of residence.[7] Studies of both Buffalo, New York, and St. Louis demonstrated a high correlation between the level of pollution in the neighborhood and the seriousness with which people viewed the problem. The 1967 ORC study found that whereas only 12 per cent of rural people and 9 per cent of persons in small towns (pop. 2,500–99,999) thought that the air pollution problem was very serious, 27 per cent of persons in communities with populations of 100,000–999,999 and 49 per cent of those living in cities with populations over 1 million ranked air pollution as very serious. Since there is generally a correlation between the size of the community and the degree of air pollution, this would tend to confirm the Buffalo and St. Louis findings.

It is more difficult to measure the degree of water pollution which exists in particular communities or neighborhoods and there are no very good data to indicate whether public concern with water pollution correlates with the severity of the problem. One would not expect a significant association between place of residence and water pollution because exposure to water pollution is not normally experienced in the home, except in those rare instances when the taste or quality of drinking water is affected.

For both air and water pollution, concern with the problem increases as one moves higher up the socio-economic scale. The higher a person's income, the more education he has had, and the higher the status of his occupation, the more likely he is to view air and water pollution as serious problems.[8] The explanation for this lies partially in the varying degrees of exposure to information media, at least in the case of air pollution. People have to be taught that air pollution is bad for their health. One may even have to be taught to consider air pollution aesthetically unattractive. Thus, unlike such problems as unemployment or crime or poor housing, perception of air pollution as a problem is heavily dependent upon exposure to channels of information; and numerous studies have shown that those with higher incomes or education are exposed to more information.

TABLE 4–3. **Perceived Seriousness of Air and Water Pollution Related to Education and Income**

	Air Pollution % "very serious"	Water Pollution % "very serious"
Education	% (n)	% (n)
Less than high school completed	23 (475)	21 (475)
High school completed	27 (363)	23 (363)
Some college	35 (199)	32 (199)
Income		
Under $5,000	21 (312)	17 (312)
$5,000–$6,999	24 (237)	19 (237)
$7,000–$9,999	31 (234)	29 (234)
$10,000 or over	33 (246)	32 (246)

Source: Opinion Research Corporation, "Public Opinion Index" (Princeton, N.J., 1968).

One irony of the air pollution situation is that if control efforts become more successful, public opinion will be increasingly more difficult to arouse. The public responds to air pollution in the form of smoke and odor, the two forms of pollution which are perceptible to the senses, but probably not the two most damaging to health. Sulfur oxides, nitrogen oxides, carbon monoxide, and other highly dangerous pollutants are neither seen nor smelled in the amounts usually found in ambient air. Thus, as initial control efforts reduce the smoke and odor problems the public may begin to believe that the problem has been solved, whereas in reality the most injurious forms of pollution may remain as prevalent as ever.

Perception of the water pollution problem probably arises from somewhat different factors than that of air pollution. Most forms of water pollution can be either seen or smelled and little education is necessary to be offended by a filthy river or angered by a sign which states that swimming is not allowed because of pollution. The correlation between high education and income and concern about the water pollution problem may relate to the differing degree of demand for various forms of recreation—swimming, fishing, sightseeing—which are likely to be endangered by pollution. Those with higher incomes engage in such activities more than those with lower incomes and thus they are more concerned about the pollution problem. In short, one might say that perception of air pollution is dependent on degree of education, whereas perception of water pollution is more dependent on amount of income.

This is not to say that perception of water pollution as a serious problem does not also depend on exposure to channels of communication. Governments at all levels and several nationwide private groups have devoted considerable time and energy in recent years to trying to convince the public of the dangers of pollution. Their success is demonstrated by the great increase in public concern in the past few years. Although degree of pollution may be the greatest single determinant of *variations* among different groups in the degree of concern about the problem, educational efforts and publicity given to the problem would seem to be the best explanation for the overall *amount* of public concern. Neither air nor water pollution has gotten so much worse in the past few years as to account for the great increase in public awareness.

What we have seen in the past few years is a common phenomenon of governmental bureaucracies supported by various interest groups utilizing large amounts of resources to bolster their own strength. The process is circular, at least up to a point, because as the bureaucracies gain support, they increase their ability to command resources of men and money, which in turn increases their ability to stimulate still further support. As the water pollution budget grows, the amount of money spent educating the public about the water pollution problem also increases.[9] And as the educational effort succeeds, it results in pressure applied to Congress and the administration to devote still more funds to water pollution control. There is nothing necessarily evil about this; it is done by almost every unit of the Federal government and by most agencies of state and local government.

The growth of public concern over the pollution problem may also involve some psychological factors. At a time when America is deeply divided on fundamental political questions, an issue like pollution which at least verbally unites everyone is not only of political value to officeseekers but also of psychological value to members of the general public. Thus people may stress concern with pollution as a way of avoiding thinking about more divisive matters. The unifying aspects of the issue are reinforced by perceptions of who or what is responsible for pollution. For many persons, at least among the more sophisticated segments of the public, pollution is a result of "technology." When technology is named as the villain nobody is offended, and "man against technology" seems to have much the same appeal that "man against nature" held in past years.

If public concern with pollution is to result in anything being done about the problem, then those who are concerned must also take some sort of constructive action. In most cases this action involves making demands upon some level of government. The wants, in other words, must be translated into demands.

DEMANDS

It requires a much higher degree of commitment and sophistication to do something about pollution (or any other public problem) than simply to worry about it. The problem must be seen as one which government or some other group can do something about; there must be knowledge about what kind of action an individual can take; and there must finally be a willingness to give the time and effort to take the action. Even if the action is only writing a letter to a congressman, these requirements are very difficult for the average American to meet.

In almost all the studies of public opinion on pollution a significant gap was found between those who were very concerned about pollution and those who had done anything about their concern.[10] The latter category was a very small percentage of the former. People were simply unaware of what could be done to control pollution. This same phenomenon probably helps to explain some of the seemingly inconsistent results obtained in various national opinion polls. When the Gallup Poll asked people in February 1968: "What do you think is the most important problem facing the country today?", the category of "sanitation: garbage, sewage" ranked a poor eleventh, considerably behind education, transportation, housing, and other issues.[11] But when people are presented with a specific list of governmental programs, air and water pollution consistently come out at or near the top in the public list of priorities. Thus the Harris Survey in April of 1967 found that more people favored expanding air and water pollution control than any other Federal programs, including aid to education, medical care, housing, and poverty.[12] The same results were obtained in a Trendex Poll in December 1967 and a Gallup Poll in October 1969.[13] In all of these polls the respondents were presented with a list of programs. It seems that when people are "cued in" to considering pollution control as a governmental activity they rate it very highly, but they do not ordinarily consider it in this light.

The Federal government and many state and local agencies have become aware of the gap between public awareness and public action. Having helped to create the awareness, they have now shifted their emphasis to forms of action. Thus HEW has issued a number of pamphlets encouraging citizens to organize pressure groups for clean air.[14]

Although specific data for pollution issues are lacking, it is probably those with more education and higher incomes who are most likely to take some kind of action to promote clean air and clean water. Studies of other issues have indicated that this is generally the case, and the anti-pollution pressure groups which have been formed in recent years seem to be made up primarily of upper- and upper-middle-class individuals.

DECISIONS

Data are not available to make any direct correlation between the state of public opinion and governmental action taken to control pollution. Even if such data were available, one would not be justified in drawing any cause-effect relationship between opinion and action. It is possible that those communities which have the most active control programs also have the most active programs to educate the public about pollution. Thus the state of public opinion might be more an effect than a cause of active local efforts to curb pollution.

It is possible to correlate data on the severity of the air pollution problem in particular localities with the amount spent by the local government for control. The result of this comparison can be seen in Table 4–4. There is little relationship between the severity of the air pollution problem and per capita local expenditures.[15] If, as we stated above, level of pollution is the major determinant of public concern, then it is clear that there are many factors other than public concern which influence the actual decisions taken by the government.

GROUPS FAVORING POLLUTION CONTROL

The most effective way for the private citizen to influence governmental action is usually through group action. The translation of individual wants into group demands is at the heart of the political process in a democratic society. Interest groups not only provide a channel for demands but may also help

TABLE 4-4. **Severity of Air Pollution Compared to Expenditures for Control**

1. SMSA	2. Cents Per Capita for Control (non-Federal funds only)	3. Expend-iture Rank*	4. Severity of AP Rank
New York	29.77	2	1
Chicago	21.69	4	2
Philadelphia	13.38	10	3
Los Angeles-Long Beach	58.94	1	4
Cleveland	27.63	3	5
Pittsburgh	16.14	9	6
Boston	4.7	11	7
Newark	0	12	8
Detroit	17.25	7	9
St. Louis (city & co.)	16.79	8	10
Gary-Hammond-E. Chicago	20.34	5	11
Akron	18.32	6	12

Source: Col. 2: 1967 expenditures from U.S. Senate, Committee on Public Works, *Air Pollution 1967,* Vol. III, pp. 1160–1283, divided by 1960 population figures taken from the U.S. Census of Population. The absence of any expenditures in Newark is due in part to the dominant role played by the state government in controlling air pollution in New Jersey. Col. 4: Ranking of severity of air pollution from U.S. Public Health Service data, reprinted in *The New York Times,* August 4, 1967, 34:2. For an explanation of the basis of the ranking, see National Center for Air Pollution Control, "A Listing of the 20 Areas with the Most Severe Air Pollution Problems," mimeographed, n.d.

*This refers to ranking among the 12 cities listed, not among all cities.

to stimulate wants and to foster the translation of wants into demands.

The major groups involved in the politics of pollution control have been conservation groups, such as the National Wildlife Federation and the Izaak Walton League; groups representing particular levels of government, such as the National Association of Counties; and the industries affected by pollution control regulations.

The conservation groups have been primarily concerned with the preservation of fish and wildlife. Because water pollution and pesticides are the two forms of pollution which tend to be most injurious to fish and wildlife, the conservation groups have tended to focus on these areas. Some of the groups have recently shown an interest in air pollution, but in almost all cases their primary concern remains the control of water pollution.

All of the conservation groups, and especially the groups devoted to the interests of fishermen, have been ardent advocates of strict water pollution control. The principles of the

Izaak Walton League of America, one of the most active groups, are representative. The official policy of the League is: "There is no sound justification for water pollution. The people of the United States are entitled to wholesome water, usable for all human needs . . . the public goal should be maximum removal of pollutants from all streams, rather than use of streams to carry an 'acceptable maximum' load of wastes." [16] This policy, it should be noted, runs contrary to the cost-benefit, community-use approach which we discussed in the first chapter.

The various conservation groups differ in their tactics and their effectiveness. The Izaak Walton League is probably the most active in lobbying for water pollution control. Its local chapters and state divisions have been quite effective in pushing for state regulation and enforcement, particularly in the Midwest.[17] Washington lobbying is left to the national headquarters, which is located in Illinois but which maintains an office in Washington.

The National Wildlife Federation is probably the largest of the conservation groups, although its estimate of 2,500,000 "supporters" represents several times the number of its actual members. The Federation issues several regular publications which are widely distributed, and it testifies frequently before congressional committees. Resolution Number One adopted at the Federation's 1968 annual convention states:

> This organization emphasizes its urgent concern about contamination of the environment by water and air pollutants, by toxic chemicals used as pesticides and for other purposes, by solid wastes, and by noise. It is believed that these conditions in the light of the human population increase, and considered collectively, constitute the most serious and pressing conservation problem of the time.[18]

In contrast to the League and the Federation, the Conservation Foundation is not a membership organization but a group which undertakes research and educational projects financed by grants and private contributions. In the past few years the Foundation has taken an increasingly active role in lobbying for conservation and pollution control measures, a shift reflected in the group's move from New York to Washington in 1965. The Foundation's monthly newsletter has become a respected source of opinion and information on pollution matters. In 1969, President Nixon named Russell Train, president of the Foundation, to be Undersecretary of the Department of the Interior, an appointment generally interpreted as an attempt to appease conservation groups angered by the appointment of Walter Hickel as Secretary of the department.

The conservation groups have been supported in their fight for water pollution control by numerous groups interested in outdoor recreation and by several major women's groups, notably the League of Women Voters. The interests of the conservation and the recreation groups tend to merge, and in fact the distinction between the two is not a very sharp one. However, certain groups, such as the Outboard Boating Club of America, the Federation of Fly Fishermen, and numerous local sportsmen's clubs, have interests which are much narrower than those of the conservation groups.

The League of Women Voters in 1956 chose water resources as a major subject for study and action. League members undertook "Know Your River Basin" surveys throughout the country, and many of the League chapters were quite influential in pushing for stronger state and local pollution control. The national League headquarters testified before Congress on a wide variety of water resource matters, including the various amendments to the Water Pollution Control Act. In 1966 the League voted to retain water resources as one of its major concerns.[19] And in 1969 the League demonstrated that it was one of the most effective of all the groups favoring pollution control. It spearheaded a "Citizens' Crusade for Clean Water" which enlisted the support of 38 organizations, including the AFL-CIO and the major conservation and municipal groups, 22 governors, and 222 members of the House of Representatives. The Crusade was aimed at getting Congress to fund the full $1 billion authorization for waste treatment grants and, although it did not succeed in getting the full authorization, it was successful in having the appropriation significantly increased.

The U.S. Conference of Mayors, the National League of Cities, and the National Association of Counties are the other major set of interests, aside from the conservation groups, supporting pollution control legislation at the national level. The cities and suburbs have been faced with the necessity of undertaking major expenditures for the laying of sewer lines and the construction of waste treatment plants. Thus their major stake in Federal legislation has been to get Washington to commit more Federal funds for these purposes. This interest coincides with that of the conservation groups, who tend to see Federal resources as the only hope for stimulating sufficient investment to curb water pollution significantly. The municipal and county groups have also looked upon Federal action as the primary means of ensuring that the pollution control efforts of one municipality will not be undercut by the lack of such efforts in a neighboring upstream community.

The groups representing local officials have had even more impact on the Federal air pollution effort than on water pollution legislation. They were the major forces pushing for strong Federal legislation, and the drafting of the 1963 Clean Air Act was done in part by Hugh Mields, who was the chief lobbyist for the U.S. Conference of Mayors.[20] Air pollution is more uniquely an urban problem than water pollution, and thus the major efforts for strong control measures have come from the big cities.

The interests of the cities have sometimes conflicted with those of the states, and state prerogatives in the pollution field have been zealously guarded by two groups of state officials—the Association of State and Territorial Health Officers and the Conference of State Sanitary Engineers. Both groups have an obvious stake in the expansion of pollution control efforts and they have been effective partners with the Federal government in promoting the cause of clean air and water. However, they have looked with disfavor on Federal encroachments into state responsibilities, particularly enforcement, and they have also discouraged attempts by Washington to deal directly with local governments.

As the relationship between air pollution and certain diseases has become clearer, several health groups have taken an active interest in air pollution control. The American Medical Association has been concerned with the problem for some time. In 1967 the National Tuberculosis Association announced the establishment of the National Air Conservation Commission, an arm of the Association devoted to the control of community air pollution. The aims of the Commission include the urging of "nationwide action for control of air pollution" and support for "the establishment of strong and effective legislation and enforcement procedures."[21]

Organizations of scientists have also taken considerable interest in pollution matters. The American Academy for the Advancement of Science has established an Air Conservation Commission to study air pollution, and other scientific organizations have urged their members to become involved in pollution control. The large role of scientific questions in pollution controversies has attracted the interest of many individual scientists, and the impact of modern technology in both causing pollution and perhaps providing a cure for it has made the issue appealing to those scientists concerned about the social implications of technological advances.

The groups discussed above have not had pollution control as their sole concern. They are groups founded for other purposes which have developed an interest in pollution control as the need for regulation became apparent. But in both air and water pollution control there have been some national groups and numerous local groups which have been founded on the basis of a concern with pollution.

The Water Pollution Control Federation brings together all those who are professionally involved in the water pollution field. It includes government officials at all levels, scientists working on pollution problems, and representatives of firms manufacturing pollution control equipment. The Federation has provided a valuable forum for the exchange of views, but because of its mixed membership it has refrained from taking any stand on controversial matters. It does not engage in lobbying activities and does not testify before congressional committees.

The Air Pollution Control Association was founded in 1907 by twelve municipal smoke inspectors who banded together under the imposing title of the International Union for the Prevention of Smoke. The membership was originally limited to smoke inspectors for fear of an industry takeover, but by 1915 the organization felt confident enough to open its ranks to all comers. In 1957, in recognition of the broader scope of the air pollution problem, the organization dropped "Smoke" from its title and became the Air Pollution Control Association. It now has 5,000 members and fourteen local sections.[22] The Association does not engage in lobbying activities, but it promotes the cause of air pollution control through various educational and publicity techniques and also provides technical assistance.

On the local scene numerous groups have been formed to combat pollution. In water pollution such groups are often concerned with water resource management generally and are organized to cover an entire watershed. However, there has been less need in water pollution than in air pollution to form local groups. Established groups, such as sportsmen's clubs and the League of Women Voters have provided the major local support for clean water.

There have not been existing organizations with strong local roots to support the cause of clean air. Such groups have had to be created on an *ad hoc* basis, and in most cases the establishment of such organizations has been a long and difficult task. Arthur Benline spent several years as Air Pollution Commissioner of New York City pleading with every group he could find to form a citizen's committee for air pollution control. He met with no response until the 1965 formation of Citizens for Clean Air, which now claims approximately 25,000 members. In most other large cities similar organizations have been formed, although there are wide variations in the strength and effectiveness of the citizen groups. The same variety can also be found among the industrial groups who become involved in the politics of pollution.

INDUSTRY

No group opposes pollution control per se. Clean air and clean water have joined the ranks of motherhood and apple pie in the American political pantheon. However, some groups are clearly more in favor of pollution control than others, or pollution control would not be a political problem. Industrial polluters tend to be at the core of much of the opposition to stringent pollution controls.

The dilemma of the polluting industry is not difficult to understand. Pollution control equipment is expensive, and it adds nothing to the value of the goods produced. Insofar as a company is in business to make money, pollution control is generally bad business. But counterbalancing the profit incentive are the forces of law and public opinion.

The power of industry to foster or retard pollution control is tremendous. This derives not primarily from its political sophistication or monetary resources but from the simple fact that the ultimate decision whether or not to cease polluting lies with each individual firm. Government can set standards and can enforce them against particularly recalcitrant firms, but without widespread cooperation on the part of industry significant pollution abatement will not be achieved. Pollution laws, like all other laws, require a high degree of voluntary compliance for their success, and thus the private sector, considered collectively, has a veto power over the progress of much pollution abatement.

The attitude of industry toward complying with pollution control regulations depends heavily on the quality and effectiveness of the regulating agency. If the agency is willing and able to enforce the regulations against polluting industries, and if the industries are reasonably sure that all competitors in the area are to be treated alike, then there will probably be a high degree of voluntary compliance.

Aside from the effectiveness of the regulatory agency, the likelihood of any particular firm abating its pollution is dependent primarily on three factors: (1) The cost of abatement in comparison with the company's resources; (2) the sensitivity of the firm to public opinion and the amount of adverse public opinion aroused by the firm's activities; and (3) the political influence possessed by the firm. The first of these factors is the most important. Public opinion and political influence will be unimportant considerations if the cost of abatement is so small as to be insignificant. If the cost is so great as to entail the bankruptcy of the business, public opinion will not be a significant factor but political influence may be very important.

Industry investment in pollution control equipment was estimated at about $1.1 billion in 1967 and was expected to be about $1.5 billion in 1968.[23] These expenditures are about evenly divided between air and water pollution control. They varied widely by type of industry, with electric and gas utilities accounting for about one-third of the total.

FWPCA has estimated that in the period 1969–73 industry will have to invest $2.6–4.6 billion for new equipment to meet state water quality standards, and that an additional $3 billion will have to be spent during the same period for operating and maintaining industrial waste treatment works.[24] The largest investment, $280 million, will be required from the chemical industry, with food processing a close second, requiring $220 million.[25] If these figures are close to correct, then industry expenditures for water pollution control are what they should be to solve the problem. This is confirmed by the 1969 FWPCA report on "The Cost of Clean Water and Its Economic Impact" which states that, "on the basis of available evidence, industry expenditures for waste treatment facilities in the last two years were close to target expenditures established in last year's report."[26]

No comparable figures are available for industrial air pollution control requirements, although NAPCA is working on a study of the costs of industry control. It would be very surprising if the industrial investment were "on target" to meet the air pollution problem. It is much more likely that there is a significant gap between air pollution control needs and industry expenditures.

Industry has lobbied intensively for governmental subsidies to offset the costs of pollution control equipment. It has been quite successful in obtaining exemption for such equipment from state taxes, and many localities have also passed legislation exempting pollution control equipment from property taxes.[27] At the Federal level the efforts for tax writeoffs or other forms of subsidy have met with more limited success because of the combined opposition of the Treasury Department and the powerful head of the House Ways and Means Committee, Wilbur Mills. The Treasury Department and Mills have both expressed the opinion that the tax structure should not be made any more complex than it now is, and that taxes should be used only as a method for raising revenue, not for any other purpose.

Most economic experts argue that tax subsidies are an inefficient method of encouraging pollution control. Such subsidies would pay only for waste treatment, but in the case of many industries it would be far more efficient to prevent the wastes from being produced by changing the manufacturing process. For example, the amount of water used in manufacturing paper or steel can be reduced by 95 per cent if certain manufacturing processes are used.[28] But since a tax subsidy would not pay for such a process change, a subsidy system would encourage the plants to produce twenty times as much pollution and then build a large "end-of-the-line" treatment plant. The treatment plant approach would be much more expensive for the government and for the society as a whole, but it might be less expensive for the manufacturer who could not get a tax writeoff for employing the more efficient process.[29] Also, most methods of giving tax credits help those who need it least by providing more credit for firms making large profits than for firms making small profits or no profit at all.

In 1966, when the 7 per cent writeoff on capital investment was suspended, industrial forces spearheaded by the steel industry succeeded in keeping the writeoff for pollution control equipment.[30] The 7 per cent credit was restored for all types of investment six months later, so that the special credit for pollution equipment was short-lived. Congressional interest in tax relief for pollution control continued, and in 1969 the same situation was repeated.[31] President Nixon recommended repeal of the 7 per cent credit without exceptions. The House Ways and Means Committee accepted the President's recommendation, but, in an effort to satisfy the intense congressional and industrial pressures, it recommended a special five-year rapid tax writeoff for pollution abatement equipment.[32]

The sensitivity of firms to public opinion depends heavily

on the character of the corporate managers and thus is difficult to generalize about. Large firms which sell to the public under their own name are generally more conscious of public relations, and such firms have often taken the initiative in publicizing the need for pollution controls.[33]

A conspicuous exception to the generalization about companies which sell to the public under their own name is the automobile industry, which has generally taken a rather callous attitude toward the pollution problem. In January 1969, the Justice Department filed suit against the four major auto manufacturers and their trade association, charging that the companies had conspired to delay the development and use of devices to control air pollution from automobiles. In September, the Federal government announced that it had agreed to settle the suit through a consent decree which would not impose any penalty on the manufacturers and would seal the grand jury records, thus closing off information that might be used in other damage suits. The case illustrates both the attitude and the power of the automobile companies.[34]

Political influence is generally a function of the size of the firm, its importance to the economy, and also probably the degree to which it is normally involved in dealing with governmental agencies. Industrial firms employ a wide variety of political strategies. For some the best defense is a good offense. Thus thirty-seven corporations in the Ohio River Valley between Ohio and West Virginia banded together as the West Virginia-Ohio Industry Committee, drafted an interstate air pollution control compact, and succeeded in having it passed by the Ohio and West Virginia legislatures.[35] While the public spiritedness of these firms is praiseworthy, there is also little doubt that one of the major reasons for the industry initiative was to ward off the Federal government, which had already held one abatement conference in the area, had promised two more, and had acquired the power to establish interstate commissions under the 1967 Air Quality Act.

The variety of defensive tactics is well illustrated by the efforts of the coal industry to combat regulations on sulfur oxide emissions. The National Coal Policy Conference used a number of tactics within the Executive Branch, including the threat to push for the transfer of the air pollution function to the Department of the Interior. Having failed in the Executive Branch, the industry representatives succeeded in having Congress make several significant alterations in the 1967 Air Quality Act, including the requirement that HEW reconsider its criteria for sulfur oxides and the addition of various provisions for greater industry representation in the enforcement and standard-setting functions. The battle then shifted to the state and local arena where the industry resorted to the courts to block sulfur regulations. In New Jersey and St. Louis the coal interests were successful in getting the courts to delay application of the regulations.

It should be clear from what has been said above that industry cannot be considered any more monolithic in relation to pollution control than it is in relation to any other major public issue. This point is underscored by the growing role of industries engaged in the manufacture of pollution control equipment. For firms which contribute to pollution, government regulation and the installation of control equipment is at best a necessary evil. However, for firms manufacturing control equipment, the more regulation the better. For example, while the automobile industry dragged its heels on the question of controlling pollution from motor vehicles, American Machine and Foundry and other potential manufacturers of afterburner equipment were lobbying for more stringent regulations which, they hoped, could be met only by the installation of the additional equipment they would produce.[36]

Pollution control is now a major industry and expanding rapidly. To the more than $1 billion spent in 1967 by industry for control equipment must be added the approximately $2 billion spent by municipalities for treatment plants and sewer lines. These figures represent a major increase over the previous year's expenditures, and there is no reason to question the statement of one authority on investments that "The overall pollution-control market may be developing into one of the most rapidly growing segments of the economy."[37]

There are, in addition to the manufacturers of control equipment, other entire industries which benefit from the regulation of pollution, and these other industries are of even more political significance and economic importance than the control equipment producers. For example, the natural gas and nuclear power industries have been beneficiaries of the campaign against high-sulfur coal and oil. Many sectors of the economy, such as commercial fishing and certain types of agriculture, are dependent on clean air and water for their continuance. All of these interests have not hesitated to push for more stringent regulation of pollution.

Interest Group Impact on Decisionmaking

Given the multitude of interest groups representing all shades of opinion on questions of pollution control it is almost impossible to isolate the effects of interest groups per se. An administrator who appears to be acting totally independently may simply be anticipating the reaction of some group or set of groups to his decision. However, we can hazard a few generalizations about interest group influence.

The influence of polluting industries tends to be greater at the state and local level than at the national level. Such industries are more important to the economy of the locality or state than to the national economy and thus have more bargaining power. They can threaten to leave the locality but they are not likely to threaten to leave the United States. The state and local governments are generally less sophisticated and have fewer political resources to draw on than does the Federal government. Also, the state and local governments must carry on a continuing relationship with the industries involved, and it is the states and localities who must take specific actions directed for or against specific groups. In contrast, the Federal government is more often involved in laying down rules of a general nature, and when it does deal with specific industries (in enforcement actions, for example) it can anticipate withdrawing from the involvement after a period of time and thus does not have to be as sensitive to the interests of the polluters.

The greater vulnerability of the state and local governments to polluters carries over to the national level by way of the local orientation of the Congress. The industries affected adversely by pollution regulation can generally find a more sympathetic ear in the Congress than they can in the Executive Branch. This is illustrated by the battle over air pollution regulations on sulfur, by the congressional rejection of national air pollution emission standards, and by the favorable attitude of Congress toward tax credits for industry. However, it should not be forgotten that it is the Congress which has steadily expanded the scope and stringency of Federal pollution control. The expansion of Federal legal authority demonstrates the determination of a majority of the Congress to push for clean air and water.

The Executive Branch is a microcosm of the competing interests in the private sector. The Commerce Department protects the interests of private business generally, the Bureau of Mines defends the coal and oil industry, the Bureau of Fish and Wildlife watches out for the conservationists, the Federal Power Commission promotes natural gas and electric power, the Department of Housing and Urban Development tries to advance the interests of the urbanists. In struggles over pollution control matters, those agencies favoring stringent control have generally come out on top. This is particularly true in air pollution where the National Air Pollution Control Administration in HEW has often been adamant in its refusal to consider the interests of the polluters. The Federal Water Pollution Control Administration has taken a similar approach, but the closer ties of the water pollution people to their state counterparts has made them somewhat more willing to consider both sides of the question.

The many groups which have some interest in pollution control, and the absence of any set of dominant groups (at least at the Federal level), has allowed the Executive Branch a comparatively free hand in proposing policies to deal with the pollution problem. We shall discuss the Executive Branch agencies in Chapter 5. The major external pressures influencing the Federal government have probably been the state and local governments, whose role we shall examine in Chapter 6.

CHAPTER 5

The Executive Branch

A MULTITUDE OF AGENCIES

THE ONE THING which can be said with certainty about the nature of the pollution problem is that it is changing rapidly. The conception of what pollution includes has changed in the past ten years and will continue to change. The concerns included under the heading of pollution vary considerably, depending upon who is compiling the list and when it is compiled.

The organization of the pollution control agencies in the Executive Branch reflects this rapid change. The organizational categories employed at the Federal level include: water pollution, air pollution, solid waste, radiological health, occupational health, and pesticides. Anyone who espouses the tenets of good administration will be repelled by the obvious overlaps and contradictions inherent in these categories. Air pollution and water pollution deal with the media through which pollutants travel; solid waste, radiological health, and pesticides deal with particular kinds of pollutants; occupational health is organized around the site at which the pollution takes place.

Such organizational inconsistencies are in part a reflection of the rapid growth and change in the pollution field. New problems and new ways of looking at old problems are occurring at an ever-increasing rate. The current search for an organizational home for noise control is a good example of this process.

As concern with noise shifted from noise in factories to noise from airplanes, agencies such as the Department of Defense, the Department of Transportation, and the National Aeronautics and Space Administration came to dominate research on the subject. The need to control all forms of noise is now beginning to be realized, and the present set of interagency committees, reflecting a piecemeal problem-by-problem approach, is giving way to demands to locate responsibility in agencies such as HEW and the Department of Housing and Urban Development which can focus on the entire range of noise problems.[1]

There is no single agency in the Federal government which has overall responsibility for pollution control. Each of the major categories of pollution control is embodied in a separate administrative unit, and the two most important units—the National Air Pollution Control Administration and the Federal Water Pollution Control Administration—are located in different departments, the former in HEW, the latter in Interior.

Within each major category of pollution there are numerous agencies which share some interest or responsibility for the problem. For example, there are approximately twenty Federal agencies which have some involvement in air pollution control. The League of Women Voters counted forty-five separate agencies with responsibility in the water resources field.[2] In a recent major controversy over the exposure of uranium miners to excess radioactivity, it was discovered that each of three Federal agencies (Interior, Labor, and the Atomic Energy Commission) had authority to enforce radiation exposure standards, and two separate units of the Public Health Service (Radiological Health and Occupational Health) were also deeply involved in the fate of the miners.

The organizational confusion which prevails in pollution control is to some extent typical of any major problem area confronted by the Federal government. In a complex interdependent society problems do not readily fit into the jurisdiction of any one agency. The political openness and decentralization of the Federal bureaucracy gives organizational form to this complexity. Each department, each bureau of each department, and each office of each bureau has its own particular set of organized interests which form a constituency to promote and defend the organizational stakes of the unit. The organizational unit, in turn, is obligated to defend the interests of its constituency.

The organizational problems in pollution control are due not only to rapid change and the agency-constituency relationship, but also to a third factor, the uncertainty as to what kind of problem pollution is, if in fact it can be considered as a single problem. We noted this factor of "issue context" when we discussed congressional organization. It is a pervasive difficulty within the Executive Branch. The Department of Housing and Urban Development considers pollution to be an urban problem, the Department of the Interior considers it to be an ecological problem, HEW considers it to be a health problem, and so forth. The lack of any agreed-upon definition of the goals or nature of pollution control encourages numerous agencies to view pollution as part of their jurisdiction.

Many proposals have been made attempting to simplify the Federal administrative arrangements for pollution control. Such proposals have been directed at two somewhat distinct ends. One set of proposals is aimed at organizationally unifying the *different types* of pollution control, and has usually taken the form of putting the major pollution agencies into a single department, such as a Department of Natural Resources, a Department of Science, or even a separate Department of Pollution Control. A variant of this is to create some kind of overall coordinating unit, such as a Council of Ecological Advisers in the Executive Office of the President. The second set of proposals is aimed at centralizing responsibility within the Executive Branch for *each type* of pollution control, thus reducing the number of agencies with an, interest in any one area such as water pollution control or radiological health. The transfer of the Federal Water Pollution Control Administration to the Department of the Interior was an effort in this direction, as was the President's letter of April 21, 1967, to the heads of twelve Federal agencies telling them that "Air pollution is primarily a health problem, and thus the primary responsibility for its control rests with the Department of Health, Education, and Welfare."[3]

Proposals to unify the different types of pollution control usually rest on one of three arguments. The first of these is what might be called "the systems rationale." This approach rests on the assumption that the pollution problem is the problem of disposing of society's wastes, and it proceeds from this assumption to an attempt to analyze the alternative methods for waste disposal available to the society. Proponents of this approach argue that by looking at "the total waste-disposal system" one can best arrive at the optimal method for controlling pollution.[4]

For some forms of pollution, such as solid wastes, the systems approach is helpful. It is also of obvious use in those cases where control of one type of pollution is achieved by creating some other type of pollution. However, the systems approach ignores the difficult question of what is the most relevant system for looking at pollution problems. The "waste-disposal system" may often be less fruitful in terms of trade-offs and formulating policy than such alternatives as the air or water pollution system, the preventive health system, or the water resource allocation system. The types of conflicts which have actually arisen within the Federal bureaucracy reinforce this point. Most of the major disputes have *not* been between agencies dealing with different types of pollution (i.e., the air pollution agency *vs.* the water pollution agency) but among the different agencies working on the same type of pollution (i.e., the Public Health Service air pollution unit *vs.* the Bureau of Mines air pollution unit). The problem of choosing the relevant system is the same as the problem of choosing the relevant issue context.

The difficulty of choosing the proper system or context is illustrated by the second major argument for unification which looks at pollution primarily as a health problem. The important factor from a health viewpoint is the "total body burden" of any single pollutant. If we examine human exposure to lead, for example, it makes no difference to health whether the lead comes from breathing (air pollution), drinking (water pollution), or eating (pesticides on food). Thus, to measure the degree of danger from pollution, one must look at all the ways in which a particular pollutant is transmitted. Also, since one pollutant may increase the harmfulness of another ("synergism"), it is necessary to look at all the different pollutants in relation to each other.

The "body-burden" justification has two drawbacks. First, it ignores all the effects of pollution except the health effect. Since there are many other significant effects, this is a serious limitation. Second, while it may be necessary to look at all pollutants and all methods of transmission for the purpose of determining the health effect, for the purpose of *controlling* pollution it is usually possible to work on only one media or one pollutant at a time. This is true both of enforcement procedures and of research on control technology.

The third unification argument is based on the concept of "ecology." Ecology is defined by the dictionary as "biology dealing with the mutual relations between organisms and their environment,"[5] and the ecological approach argues that since all things in nature are interrelated and pollution alters these relationships in numerous ways, pollution should be controlled to the maximum extent possible. The comparatively primitive state of the branch of biology dealing with ecology and the uncertain meaning of "natural balance" in a world which is increasingly subject to human manipulation and influence have, however, led to considerable vagueness and confusion as to what the ecological approach entails. For example, *The New York Times* in a recent editorial stated that New Jersey would benefit if the Hackensack Meadows "now filled with swamp grass and garbage dumps, were converted into an urban complex with residential, industrial and recreational facilities for 300,000 people. Unquestionably, many problems would need solution, among them measures to safeguard the ecological balance of the area."[6]

The perspective provided by ecology is an important one. Pollution clearly affects the environment, usually adversely, and some of the consequences of these changes may not only be highly injurious but also irreversible. Much more effort needs to be put into specifying the actual ecological effects of pollution. Organizationally, the ecological approach may be a useful one, particularly if an arbitrary distinction is made between human beings and the rest of nature. Many ecologists now look upon men as somewhat unwelcome intruders into the natural order. An agency which had nonhuman ecological concerns as its central focus could look at pollution effects in a comprehensive way, but could avoid the health problems raised by pollution and the dilemmas raised by trading off fish and wildlife against human life.

There is a definite need to unify the Federal government's pollution control effort, at least with respect to the setting of standards. Both the "body-burden" and the ecological argument provide a basis for unifying the standard-setting function. The current method, based primarily on the medium (air, water, food, etc.) through which a particular pollutant travels, results in many types of problems being overlooked. A good example of this is the recent decision of the Food and Drug Administration to approve the use of polyvinyl chloride (PVC) in food containers. When burned in incinerators, PVC produces hydrochloric acid and this is a serious environmental hazard. But the Food and Drug Administration was concerned only with whether the substance contaminates food and thus did not take into account the potential air pollution threat from widespread use of PVC.[7]

We shall return to the overall problem of organization, but it is first necessary to examine in greater detail the existing administrative arrangements for dealing with air and water pollution control.

AIR POLLUTION

The Federal air pollution control effort dates back to the early part of this century when the Bureau of Mines in the Department of the Interior began conducting research into means of controlling excess smoke emissions. The Bureau of Mines established an Office of Air Pollution and then later abolished it, but the Bureau has continued to maintain an interest in controlling pollution from coal and oil.[8]

The efforts by Los Angeles to control its pollution and the Donora episode focused national attention on air pollution, as we have seen. In December 1949, President Truman requested the Secretary of the Interior to organize an inter-departmental committee which would call the first United States Technical Conference on Air Pollution, and in May 1950 the conference was held in Washington;[9] 1950 also saw the first resolutions introduced in Congress calling for research into the health hazards of air pollution. As the problem came to be viewed primarily as a threat to health, the Public Health Service (PHS) was increasingly considered the proper agency to take the lead in research and control efforts.

In the early post-World War II years the PHS concern with air pollution was centered in its Division of Industrial Hygiene. In 1960 PHS combined two existing units and created a Division of Air Pollution headed by Vernon G. MacKenzie, a sanitary engineer. In 1966 the name of the division was changed to the National Center for Air Pollution Control (NCAPC) but the Center still suffered from an acute case of bureaucratic layering. It was one of five units under the Bureau of Disease Prevention and Environmental Control, which in turn was one of four bureaus under PHS, which in turn was one of eight independent units reporting to the Secretary of HEW. This situation did not prevent, indeed it encouraged, the Director of NCAPC to by-pass the hierarchy and deal directly with the Secretary's office.

In the 1968 reorganization of HEW, PHS as an organizational entity was abolished and the problem of layering somewhat relieved. NCAPC has become the National Air Pollution Control Administration (NAPCA), and is one of three major units in a newly created Consumer Protection and Environmental Health Service. The head of the service reports through the Assistant Secretary for Health to the Secretary of HEW. It is too early to tell what the political realities of the new organizational arrangement will be, but if NAPCA continues to grow in size and importance there will be increasing pressure to eliminate at least one of the intermediaries between the head of NAPCA and the Secretary of HEW.

Under the pressure of public opinion and new legislation the air pollution unit has changed from being a typical old-line PHS agency. At least up until 1960 the PHS air pollution people viewed themselves as providers of neutral competence to the state and local agencies. They considered research and the provision of technical assistance to be their primary missions. Regulatory activities were strictly the province of the sub-Federal levels. However, the need for a more active Federal role, even if such activity involves some alienation of the traditional PHS constituency of the state health departments, has now been accepted by NAPCA.

The HEW budget for air pollution control has grown extraordinarily rapidly, particularly since passage of the 1963 Clean Air Act.[10] About half of the air pollution budget is

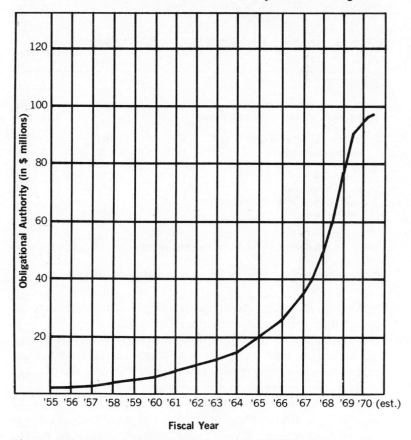

Fig. 5–1. Federal Spending for Air Pollution Control (HEW Only)

Source: The Budget of the U.S. Government, Fiscal Years 1957–70 (Washington, D.C.: G.P.O.)

directed toward research, the other half going toward abate-ment, technical assistance, and training activities.[11]

The major emphases in the past year have been on strength-ening the capability of state and local governments to enable them to assume the burdens placed on them by the 1967 Air Quality Act and on research directed toward the control of sulfur oxides pollution. The need to strengthen subnational levels of government will be discussed in greater detail in the next chapter. The sulfur problem has been the most controversial aspect of the whole air pollution effort; some of the complexi-ties of this issue will be examined in Chapter 8.

TABLE 5–1. **Allocation of HEW Air Pollution Budget**

Activity	(000 of dollars) 1968	(000 of dollars) 1969
1. Abatement and control		
(a) Grants	17,021	22,755
(b) Direct operations	4,370	8,861
2. Research, development, and demon-stration		
(a) Grants and contracts	7,641	24,701
(b) Direct operations	14,327	20,943
3. Manpower training		
(a) Grants	2,706	3,159
(b) Direct operations	1,251	1,900
4. Program direction and management services	2,280	2,500
Total	49,596*	84,819*

Source: The Budget of the U.S. Government, Fiscal Year 1970 (Washington, D.C.: G.P.O.), Appendix, p. 372.

*Totals are not the same as appropriation amounts because of financing adjustments.

Among the other agencies carrying on activities related to air pollution, the most important is the Bureau of Mines in the Department of the Interior. Mines spent approximately $2 million in 1967 on research to control air pollution from fuel combustion and it is acknowledged that the Bureau has considerable expertise in the pollution field. The Bureau is also the repository for information on the coal and oil industry and thus is the starting point for any examination of the economic effects of air pollution regulations. Interior's legisla-tive mandate calls for it to be responsible for assuring the nation of adequate fuel supplies at the lowest reasonable cost, and it is this mandate which accounts for the department's interest in air pollution control.

Since the early 1950's, when Interior lost its role as the primary air pollution agency to HEW, there has been considerable friction and rivalry between the two departments. In recent years relations between NAPCA and the Bureau of Mines have steadily deteriorated, to the point where each agency now seems to go out of its way to ignore the advice and interests of the other. In February 1969 John O'Leary, the Director of the Bureau of Mines, told the House Appropriations Committee, "We find we are not masters of our house in our air pollution work. . . . It means, as far as I am concerned, a head-on confrontation between Interior's responsibilities with respect to the resources and HEW's responsibilities with regard to air purity." [12] The Interior-HEW rivalry is one more example of the instability of jurisdictions and the number of different interests involved in the pollution problem.

The variety of interests can also be shown by the many other agencies which play a role in air pollution control. Air pollution is greatly influenced by patterns of wind and weather, and the study of such patterns is the responsibility of the Environmental Sciences Services Administration in the Department of Commerce. ESSA has about 20 meteorologists financed by HEW assigned full-time to HEW's air pollution program, and it also carries out research and observation activities which are closely related to air pollution. Air pollution does considerable damage to agricultural crops, and therefore the Department of Agriculture conducts research, primarily on contract with PHS, on the agricultural effects of pollution. Agriculture has been eager to initiate an independent program for controlling air pollution from rural sources, but has been discouraged from doing so. The Federal Power Commission has been forced to consider air pollution as a factor in the allocation of natural gas pipelines, and the Commission is also concerned about the impact of air pollution regulations on the electric power industry.

The Department of Transportation (DOT) has had an active interest in air pollution regulations affecting automobiles, as has the Interstate Commerce Commission in regulations affecting trucks and buses. The Air Quality Act of 1967 calls for DOT to administer state inspection programs to check on the maintenance of air pollution control devices in automobiles. The Department of State has been most concerned about the impact of air pollution regulations on the international fuel market, particularly on U.S. imports of residual fuel oil from Venezuela. In a related effort, the Office of Emergency Planning has been reexamining U.S. oil import policy in the light of air pollution control regulations. The Department of Housing and Urban Development is conducting research into air pollution factors in city planning and mass transit. The Department of Defense maintains a large effort to control pollution from its own facilities and also conducts research (such as the development of an electric vehicle) related to air pollution control.

The Tennessee Valley Authority has cooperated with HEW in demonstration projects for controlling pollution and, beginning in 1968, has conducted its own research on control techniques. The Post Office Department and the General Services Administration have also taken considerable interest in utilizing Federal procurement policies to further air pollution control, and the Post Office has done some experimentation on control devices with its own vehicles. The Council of Economic Advisers is working with HEW on a study of economic incentives for air pollution control. The Office of Science and Technology has been given some responsibility for overseeing air pollution research and will have a significant voice in air pollution control policy under its presidential mandate to coordinate government energy policy.

The above listing of Federal activities related to air pollution is far from complete. It should be noted that each of the agencies is involved in air pollution because the problem impinges on some primary mission of the agency. Each can point to a legislative or presidential mandate justifying its involvement.

WATER POLLUTION

The beginnings of the Federal water pollution program date back to 1912, when the Public Health Service was explicitly authorized by Congress to investigate the pollution of navigable streams and lakes. The investigations were prompted by the frequent outbreaks of typhoid fever in urban areas attributed to water supplies.[13]

Until passage of the 1956 Water Pollution Control Act, almost all of the water pollution control work remained at the state level. As Murphy states, "Through the 1950's the federal government largely confined itself to congratulating states upon their work and their compacts, to conducting river basin surveys and other research work to assist the existing state agencies, and to carrying on a program of public education."[14] The only significant exception to this was the financial help in the construction of waste treatment facilities which the Federal government provided during the New Deal period.

When the 1948 Federal act was passed, PHS established a Division of Water Pollution Control. The division quickly acquired certain characteristics and ways of doing business which were to characterize it at least until its transfer to the Department of the Interior in 1966. The division, like most of the rest of PHS, believed in working primarily through the state health departments. It did not believe that the Federal government should work directly with localities, and it was convinced that the initiative in controlling water pollution should rest with the states, not with the Federal government. The internal administrative workings of the division reflected this philosophy. Emphasis was placed on field installations, and the central headquarters in Washington was small and exercised little control. Partly as a result of this, there was little coordination among the component units of the division. The enforcement people did not talk to the technical assistance people, the research program was not tied to the control program, the grants were distributed without much thought being given to the operating needs of the agency.

The division both benefited and suffered from a considerable amount of congressional interest in its administration. The large component of public construction in the water pollution program was bound to attract congressional interest, but such concern went beyond the waste treatment grant construction program. For example, beginning with the 1948 act's authorization of a water pollution control laboratory in Cincinnati, Ohio, the Congress in succeeding acts specified the number and location of the field laboratories of the water pollution agency. The 1961 act authorized seven such laboratories, with the relevant committees informing PHS of exactly where the laboratories were to go. Not surprisingly, several of the "recommended" locations coincided with the districts of key congressmen.[15]

The reluctance of PHS to come into conflict with the state health agencies, as well as the low status of the Division of Water Pollution within the HEW hierarchy, led to congressional agitation to change the status of the water pollution agency. There was pressure for the creation of a separate Water Pollution Control Administration within HEW in 1961; but, deferring to the views of Secretary Ribicoff, Congress contented itself with the modest change of transferring the authority under the Water Pollution Control Act from the Surgeon General to the Secretary of HEW.[16]

As the Congress began to consider the water quality standards provisions which were to become law in 1965, pressure for administrative change increased. If the Federal government was to review and approve state water quality standards, it was clear that the agency doing the reviewing and giving the approval would have to be willing to bargain and to risk antagonizing the state agencies. A number of other changes in the nature of the water pollution control program had also reinforced the desire for change. It had become clear that health considerations were a comparatively insignificant factor in the contemporary problem of water pollution, and it thus seemed anomalous to have the authority for the program vested in the nation's health agency. Some critics charged that the doctors who ran PHS slighted the water program because of its lack of importance for public health. It was also becoming clear, at least to the administration, that more emphasis should be placed on organizing the program on a river basin basis and tying it more closely to the other water resource activities of the government. PHS had been conducting studies of entire river basins for years, but the impact of such studies on the pollution control program was minimal.

The combined pressure of these considerations led to the authorization in the 1965 amendments to the Water Pollution Control Act of a Federal Water Pollution Control Administration (FWPCA) which would remain in HEW but would report directly to the Secretary and be independent of PHS. (This proposal had been made as early as 1959 by Rep. Blatnik.)[17] Both the Secretary of HEW and the White House remained silent on the merits of the new organizational arrangement.

It was destined to have a short life. The act was signed by the President on October 2, 1965. Five months later, on February 28, 1966, the President submitted to Congress a reorganization plan transferring the newly created FWPCA from HEW to the Department of the Interior.[18] The reorganization plan took effect, with the assent of Congress, on May 10, 1966.

There are numerous conflicting accounts of how and why the transfer proposal was made. It seems clear that the initiative for the move come directly from President Johnson, under prodding from Interior Secretary Udall.[19] The President gave his full backing to the transfer despite opposition from Senator Muskie, the Budget Bureau, and other influential sectors. HEW Secretary Gardner, who had assumed office only six months before the decision, indicated that he was not prepared to fight to retain the agency. After leaving office he reportedly stated that he regretted this decision more than any other he had made during his tenure as Secretary.

The timing of the proposal was influenced by the 1965 Water Quality Act and the process of formulating the 1966 Clean Water Act. The major disruption in the water pollution agency resulting from its removal from PHS was the loss to the agency of large numbers of high-level scientific personnel who declined to resign their commissions in the PHS commissioned officers corps. The White House calculated that since this loss was attributable to passage of the 1965 act, a further transfer of the agency would not cause significantly more disruption.

The 1966 act was being formulated within the Executive Branch at the time the decision was made to transfer FWPCA to Interior. The emphasis which the legislation gave to river basins was more consistent with Interior's method of operations than with HEW's. This was made dramatically clear at a key White House meeting to discuss the 1966 bill. Udall came to the meeting personally and presented a well-designed scheme for river basin agencies. HEW was represented by lower level personnel who gave the impression that they had not given much thought to the problem. From that point on, the major staff work on the 1966 bill was done by Interior, not by HEW.

Several accommodations were made to smooth the passage of the reorganization plan. It was agreed informally that HEW, in exchange for surrendering the water pollution control function to Interior, would acquire the education and welfare functions of Interior's Bureau of Indian Affairs. Due to a number of factors this agreement never was brought to fruition. More importantly, the White House and congressional leaders agreed that Muskie's subcommittee of the Public Works Committee should retain jurisdiction in the Senate over water pollution legislation.

The primary emphasis in the water pollution control program since its transfer to Interior has been on the review and approval of the state water quality standards. However, the program reveals its PHS genesis in the heavy emphasis placed on grants and on research activities.[20] The FWPCA research program differs from the air pollution program in that considerably more FWPCA funds are directed toward demonstrations, particularly demonstrations of advanced waste treatment technology, methods of controlling industrial wastes, and methods of controlling sewer overflow from storm waters. The percentage of funds going to support small undirected research activities is much lower for water pollution than for air pollution. This is primarily due to the more primitive "state of the art" in the air pollution field.

Another major difference between the air and water pollution programs is the large effort which FWPCA devotes to comprehensive planning activities. This effort is part of a multi-agency (Interior, Corps of Engineers, Agriculture, and HEW) program to develop comprehensive plans for most of the twenty major river basins into which the country has been divided. The work of the agencies is coordinated by the Water Resources Council, established under the Water Resources Planning Act of 1965.[21] So far, there is little evidence to indicate that the comprehensive plans have had any impact on the water pollution control program.

The FWPCA budget for research, enforcement, and planning is overshadowed by the funds distributed in grants for the construction of waste treatment works.[22] If one excludes the waste treatment grants, the FWPCA budget is just about the same size as the air pollution budget, although its growth has been less rapid. Including the waste treatment grants, the water pollution budget is more than nine times as large as the air pollution budget.

Many other agencies have activities bearing directly on water pollution control. In a remarkable demonstration of the deficiencies of the legislative process, the administration in 1965

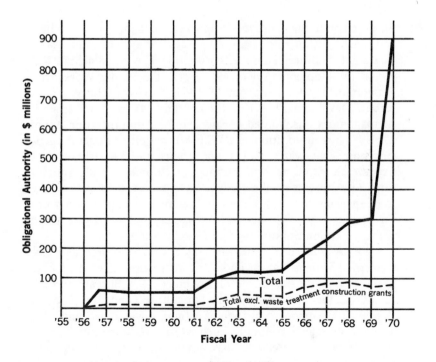

Fig. 5–2. Federal Spending for Water Pollution Control (FWPCA only)

Source: The Budget of the U.S. Government, Fiscal Years, 1957–1969 (Washington, D.C.: G.P.O.) and 1970 appropriations acts.

TABLE 5–2.
Allocation of Interior Water Pollution Budget
(excluding waste treatment grants and buildings and facilities)

Activity	(000 of dollars) 1968	(000 of dollars) 1969
1. Enforcement	3,393	3,587
2. Research, development, and demonstration		
(a) Grants and contracts	41,533	33,472
(b) Direct operations	9,882	10,197
3. Planning, assistance, and training activities		
(a) Grants	14,100	15,250
(b) Direct operations	18,463	19,062
4. Executive direction and support	4,811	5,282
Total	92,182	86,850

Source: The Budget of the U.S. Government, Fiscal Year 1970, Appendix, p. 641, and information supplied to the author by FWPCA.

proposed and the Congress approved no less than four new acts each authorizing Federal grants for sewers and waste treatment facilities. These acts were: (1) The Appalachian Regional Development Act of 1965;[23] (2) the Public Works and Economic Development Act of 1965;[24] (3) the Housing and Urban Development Act of 1965;[25] and (4) the 1965 amendments to the Consolidated Farmers Home Administration Act of 1961.[26] Thus in addition to FWPCA three other Federal agencies now give water and sewer grants—the Departments of Commerce, Housing and Urban Development, and Agriculture. The Bureau of the Budget has succeeded in getting the four agencies to use a common preliminary application form for localities seeking Federal assistance, but otherwise there is little coordination among the four programs.

FWPCA must deal with the major water resource agencies concerned with irrigation and the construction of dams. These agencies include the Corps of Engineers, the Bureau of Reclamation, the Department of Agriculture, and the Federal Power Commission. Irrigation is a major water use and also a major source of pollutants such as salt, sediment, and pesticides. Interior's Bureau of Reclamation is busy encouraging irrigation and thus contributing to pollution, while Interior's FWPCA is busy trying to clean the pollution up.

The water resource construction agencies, notably the Corps of Engineers, have in recent years used water quality storage benefits as a useful rationale for justifying dam and reservoir projects. The Corps is required to justify each of its projects by analyzing costs and benefits. It has found that the cost-benefit ratio of some projects can be made much more attractive by adding the value of reservoir water used to augment the flow downstream to dilute pollution. This is a laudable case of an agency taking into account interests other than its primary mission. However, the benefits to the Corps are obvious (it allows them to build more projects), and the fact that neither the polluters nor the states and localities share in the cost of water quality storage has been the subject of some discussion.[27]

In important respects the water pollution control program is a recreation program, since one of its major purposes is to improve and protect the quality of water so that it may be used for recreational purposes. Many other Federal agencies have an interest in recreation, including three agencies within the Interior Department—the Bureau of Outdoor Recreation, the National Park Service, and the Fish and Wildlife Service. The Forest Service and the Soil Conservation Service, both part of the Department of Agriculture, and the Open-Space Program, under the aegis of the Department of Housing and Urban Development, also have some stake in the recreational aspects of water pollution control.

Research on the effects and control of water pollution, like every other major part of the problem, involves a number of different Federal agencies. Aside from FWPCA, two other units in the Department of the Interior—the Office of Water Resources Research and the Office of Saline Water—conduct research on water pollution control. The Department of Agriculture conducts research on rural sources of pollution. And, most importantly, under the terms of the reorganization plan which put FWPCA in Interior, responsibility for "the health effects" of water pollution remains in HEW. A not very successful attempt to clarify this division of responsibility was made by an interagency agreement negotiated shortly after the approval of the reorganization. In practice the division of responsibility has meant that HEW retains its traditional concern about municipal drinking water supplies while FWPCA worries about "raw" water, i.e. water before it is pumped into municipal systems. However, as FWPCA increasingly becomes involved in developing "closed treatment systems" which purify waste water to such a degree that it can be used over again, the distinction between "raw" and "finished" water may become increasingly difficult to make, so that the basis of the agreement is undermined. Also, if viruses and chemicals in water become widely recognized as a health problem, HEW's role in water pollution will be increased and coordination between Interior and HEW further complicated.

COORDINATING MECHANISMS

Given the numerous Federal agencies involved in pollution control, coordination within the Executive Branch is a constant and troublesome problem. Much effort is expended in trying to resolve conflicts among agencies and attempting to harness the collective power of the Federal government to work for common ends.

Much of the communication between Federal agencies takes place informally at the working levels of the bureaucracy. The off-the-cuff phone call to an acquaintance in another agency or the chance meeting at a professional conference may be what keep the system functioning. But more formal mechanisms are also required to permit the formulation of policy and to arrive at official solutions to problems.

In both air pollution and water pollution there is clearly a lead agency—a department which has been given the major part of the statutory authority and whose leadership in the field has been recognized by the President. This solves many potential problems and reduces the likelihood of the often chaotic relationships which can exist in such areas as pesticides or occupational health where no one agency is charged with leadership. However, the fundamental weakness of the lead agency arrangement is the same problem that affects most Federal coordinating mechanisms—the parity of the Federal departments. Although HEW is acknowledged as *the* Federal agency in the air pollution field, it still has no real power over other Federal departments in air pollution matters or anything else. Neither legally nor politically is it anything more than an equal.

One modification of the equality among agencies is found when the lead agency channels funds to other agencies. HEW gives money from its own budget to more than a half dozen other agencies for the performance of various tasks. In some cases exchange of personnel may also be involved, as in the case of the Environmental Sciences Services Administration, which provides NAPCA with a unit of meteorologists on a full-time basis. The lead agency serving as a conduit of funds has had mixed success in the air pollution program. It has worked quite well in most cases, but has led to frequent and sometimes acrimonious disputes between NAPCA and the Bureau of Mines. The disputes have been over such matters as the different research priorities held by the two agencies and the degree of control to be exercised by NAPCA over the conduct of the Bureau of Mines research.

Perhaps the most common mechanism for coordination has been the interagency committee. The shortcomings of such committees have been well explored.[28] The most important issues tend not to be discussed, and those that are considered are resolved by resorting to the lowest common denominator of agreement. The Committee on Water Resources Research, an interagency group which attempts to coordinate and assign priorities for various aspects of water research, has suffered from these and other problems. The committee has, for the past several years, come up with an agreed schedule, including specific dollar figures, for each agency's water research program. However, it has been unable to make its decisions stick when agency budgets have been considered by the Budget Bureau and the Congress. Even if the Budget Bureau and the Congress were to accord very high status to the committee's recommendations (which they do not because of the inevitable logrolling and lack of perspective which characterize the committee's work), the decentralized nature of the budget process would make it unlikely that the committee's programs would survive intact. There is no mechanism in the Budget Bureau or the Congress which can pull the water research program together. In short, any serious attempt at regular coordination runs so counter to the general characteristics of the Federal government that the cards are heavily stacked against its success.

Formal interagency agreements are frequently negotiated and signed between agencies. The agreements have limited usefulness because of the often rapid change in the types of problems dealt with by the agencies. Such agreements also tend to have the same characteristics as the deliberations of interagency committees. The major issues are avoided or are dealt with so circumspectly that the document is incomprehensible to those not familiar with the outstanding controversies. Examples of avoidance of issues can be found in almost any agreement. Typical is the agreement between HEW and Interior on the health aspects of water pollution control.[29] One major point of dispute was whether HEW should be permitted to construct experimental pilot plants for water purification, since Interior was already constructing such plants as part of its advanced waste treatment program. The interagency agreement states:

> To avoid duplication of Federal installations for pilot plants, when such facilities are required to study methods of removing contaminants from drinking water, Public Health Service personnel may use Department of the Interior facilities. To assure that such installations will adequately serve such purposes, the Department of the Interior shall consult with the Department of Health, Education, and Welfare in their design.[30]

This wording leaves the question of HEW authority to build its own plants completely open.

We have already discussed the centralization of pollution control functions as a possible solution to the problem of coordination. We also mentioned earlier the proposals made for some coordinating mechanism at a level higher than the agency one, in the Executive Office of the President, for example. The Bureau of the Budget, which is part of the Executive Office, attempts to coordinate agencies as part of its regular job. In May 1969 President Nixon established a cabinet-level Environmental Quality Council.[31] The Council, which was given a very broad mandate to review, coordinate, and initiate environmental policies, consists of six department heads and the Vice-President. Its meetings are presided over by the President, and the President's science adviser serves as Executive Secretary.

On January 1, 1970, the President signed legislation creating a three-man Council on Environmental Quality in the Executive Office.[32] The administration had originally opposed the creation of such a statutory body, but now that it has come into existence, it will undoubtedly become a central focus for consideration of new ideas, resolution of governmental conflicts, and other pressures generated by the great increase in governmental and public concern over environmental issues. The Council has an extremely small staff which may be overwhelmed by the tasks which it is expected to perform. A more serious long-term danger is that the Council's role as intimate adviser to the President, a role which gives the group its only real power, will be eroded by the Council being forced to make concessions to a very active, diffuse, and unpredictable constituency of anti-pollution forces both within and outside the bureaucracy. The Council cannot serve two masters, but to ignore either the President or the anti-pollution constituency invites grave dangers.

There are no easy answers to the problems raised by the multitude of agencies in the pollution field. The problems reflect the pluralistic pattern of American politics, the general complexity of policy issues in an urbanized, industrialized society, and the particular complexities of pollution. Although improvements in administrative efficiency and coordination are certainly possible, these underlying factors of pluralism and complexity are not likely to change.

CHAPTER 6

State and Local Government

POLLUTION CONTROL at the state and local level must function in a setting of numerous governments competing for economic advancement and divided between polluters and the victims of pollution, between central cities and suburbs, and between Republicans and Democrats. All of the governments are short of funds and thus reluctant to invest in the public facilities necessary to curb pollution. The financial squeeze also intensifies the competition for industrial ratables, a competition which in many cases results in a reluctance to impose strict pollution control regulations.

The difficulty of achieving stringent pollution control at the local level and the regional nature of the pollution problem have resulted in a steadily greater assumption of responsibility by higher levels of government. The states now have major responsibility for air and water pollution control, but their limited jurisdiction and the obstacles to interstate cooperation make a stronger Federal role increasingly likely.

RESPONSIBILITY FOR WATER POLLUTION CONTROL

Attempts to control water pollution in the United States date back almost to the beginning of the new nation. During the colonial period cities passed regulations governing the disposal of sewage, and a few of the more progressive communities invested in municipal sewer lines.[1] In the first half of the nineteenth century numerous state statutes and local ordinances were passed, dealing with nuisances and hazards to navigation arising from floating debris and other forms of water pollution. And in the 1870's and 1880's, as the relationship between contagious diseases and water pollution became known, states created boards of health which devoted much of their effort to water purification and the prevention of pollution.

Throughout the nineteenth century, although most state legislatures enacted water pollution statutes, 'the primary responsibility for pollution control rested with the local governments. The states delegated to local units of government the power to prevent or abate pollution and authorized local officials to enforce the state pollution laws through criminal prosecution. The authority of local government was supplemented by state authorization for aggrieved individuals to institute civil suits for damages caused by pollution.[2] These approaches to pollution control proved inadequate. The localities were unable to control pollution coming from upstream, and they had no incentive to control their own pollution. Individuals found it almost impossible to bring civil suits because of the difficulty of proving who was responsible for the damage.

The failure of local control efforts and the concern with typhoid and other waterborne diseases began to lead toward the centralization of pollution control responsibility at the state level. By 1948, every state had assumed responsibility for water pollution and most states had placed the administration of the program in the state health department. Beginning about 1950, the increased emphasis placed on water pollution control and the lessened importance of the health aspects of pollution began to affect state administrative arrangements. Independent pollution control agencies were created, or separate statutory agencies within the health department were established. By 1968, only twenty-one state health departments retained authority for water pollution control.[3] Most of the New England and Southern States had established separate commissions or boards to deal with the water pollution problem, whereas the Midwest and Western states were more likely to retain responsibility in the state health department.

The authority of state water pollution control agencies is

often limited by the same kinds of interagency jurisdictional problems which plague the Federal government. In almost all states, the health department retains some responsibility for municipal water supplies. The fish and game department has a stake in the control of pollution, as does the parks or recreation department. Several states have created water resource agencies, which in some cases have jurisdiction over water pollution and in other cases do not. In many states coordination is attempted by the creation of a water pollution control board which includes representatives from the interested agencies; but many such boards also have significant industry representation, a practice which does not encourage strong enforcement efforts.[4]

TABLE 6-1. **State Water Pollution Control**

State	1. Agency	2. 1969 Budget (in $000; incl. Fed. grants)	3. 1969 Personnel (in man-years)
Ala.	Water Improvement Comm'n.	188	24
Alaska	Dept. of Health & Welf.	48	10
Ariz.	Dept. of Health	122	13
Ark.	Pollution Control Comm'n.	257	29
Calif.	Water Resources Control Board	3,400	194
Colo.	Water Pollution Control Comm'n.	168	18
Conn.	Water Resources Comm'n.	394	57
Del.	Air & Water Resources Comm'n.	210*	26
Fla.	Board of Health	450*	68
Ga.	Water Quality Control Board	343	38
Hawaii	Dept. of Health	115	26
Idaho	Dept. of Health	70*	9
Ill.	Sanitary Water Board	1,003	79
Ind.	Stream Pollution Control Board	662	74
Iowa	Dept. of Health	228	36**
Kan.	Dept. of Health	436	38
Ky.	Water Pollution Control Comm'n.	368	37
La.	Stream Control Comm'n.	285	17
Maine	Water & Air Envt'l Improvement Comm'n.	205	18
Md.	Dept. of Health & Dept. of Water Resources	1,105	96
Mass.	Water Resources Comm'n.	326	12
Mich.	Water Resources Comm'n.	730*	74
Minn.	Pollution Control Agency	356	46
Miss.	Air & Water Pollution Control Comm'n.	215	19
Mo.	Water Pollution Board	377	30
Mont.	Board of Health	105	7

State	1. Agency	2. 1969 Budget (in $000; incl. Fed. grants)	3. 1969 Personnel (in man-years)
Nebr.	Water Pollution Control Council	113	13
Nev.	Dept. of Health & Welfare	54	8
N.H.	Water Supply & Pollution Control Comm'n.	315	48
N.J.	Dept. of Health	1,052	48
N.M.	Dept. of Public Health	105	12**
N.Y.	Dept. of Health	1,590	300
N.C.	Dept. of Water Resources	479	52
N.D.	Dept. of Health	55	9
Ohio	Dept. of Health	878	46
Okla.	Dept. of Health	197	21
Ore.	State Sanitary Authority	180*	40
Pa.	Dept. of Health	940*	216
R.I.	Dept. of Health	238	27
S.C.	Water Pollution Control Authority	257	36
S.D.	Dept. of Health	78	20
Tenn.	Stream Pollution Control Board	298	33
Tex.	Water Quality Board	946	89
Utah	Water Pollution Control Board	105	12
Vt.	Dept. of Water Resources	215	20
Va.	Water Control Board	493	75
Wash.	State Pollution Control Comm'n.	803	66
W.Va.	Dept. of Natural Resources	288	29
Wis.	Dept. of Resources Devel.	1,239	118
Wyo.	Dept. of Public Health	51	3
Total		23,135	2,436
Median		293	31.5

Source: Col. 1: FWPCA, "State WPC Agencies" (January 1968); Cols. 2 and 3: state water pollution control plans on file with FWPCA, Washington, D.C.

*Estimated.
**1968 figures.

NOTE: Due to differences in interpretation and terminology on the part of the states, the above figures are not strictly comparable in all cases.

In recent years a significant portion of the funds spent by state water pollution control agencies has come from the Federal government. In 1968 almost half the money spent by state agencies came from Federal grants. The Federal grants go entirely to state and interstate agencies, and not to local agencies.

Until recently, the financing of waste treatment plants was left largely in the hands of the local communities, although a few states made modest contributions to the cost of construction, and the Federal government contributed up to 30 per cent of the cost in some cases. This arrangement is being changed by two events. First, the 1966 Clean Water Act authorized the Federal government to pay up to 55 per cent of the cost of building treatment plants, providing the states contributed 25 per cent of the cost and met certain other conditions. Eventually most of the states will probably contribute 25 per cent in order to take advantage of the larger Federal share.[5] Thus the localities will be left having to pay only 20 per cent, if sufficient appropriations are provided to implement the Federal and state statutes.

The second event was the development by Governor Rockefeller and the approval by the New York State voters in 1965 of a $1 billion "Clean Waters" bond issue. The size of the bond issue was impressive enough, but it was the method of financing that proved most influential. The Rockefeller plan in essence put New York in the position of prefinancing the Federal government's contributions to waste treatment construction within the state. The state agreed to make funds available to the localities as if the Federal government had paid its full share; the state would then attempt to recover the amount of the Federal share when Congress appropriated sufficient funds.

The Rockefeller plan was designed to meet two problems—the lag in Federal appropriations and the rapidly rising costs of waste treatment construction. It permitted the localities within a state to proceed immediately with construction rather than waiting until Federal funds were available. The New York State approach is being considered by several other states, and it received indirect sanction in the 1966 Federal act which authorized states to collect retroactively on construction grants.[6]

From the beginning of the Federal waste treatment grant program in 1956, through September 30, 1969, Federal grants have amounted to $1.37 billion and local communities have contributed an additional $4.75 billion.[7] Although these figures indicate that local governments are spending approximately $4 for every Federal dollar, the situation varies considerably from state to state. Some states do not use the full amount of Federal funds allocated to them; while in many others the actual ratio of local to Federal spending is higher than 4 to 1. For example, in New Jersey over the past ten years, less than

15 per cent of the money spent for construction of waste treatment plants came from the Federal government. Until the 1966 act, the Federal grant program strongly favored smaller communities, both in the allocation of funds and in the percentage of costs paid. Thus the more urbanized states had a much lower percentage of their total construction outlay paid by the Federal government.

The allocation of Federal waste treatment construction grants within any given state is supposed to be done in accordance with a state water pollution control plan.[8] However, state plans for water pollution control are more fiction than reality. The Federal government does not review the state plans, and within many states political pressures are more important than planning in determining which localities receive priority for the grants. In most states arbitrary formulas, such as "first come, first served," are used in approving grant applications in an attempt to minimize local political pressure on the state government. Little or no attempt is made to determine which treatment plants produce the most benefits or will be most effective in controlling pollution.[9]

The 1965 Federal Water Quality Act placed responsibility on each of the fifty states for formulating water quality standards for interstate waters and for drawing up a comprehensive plan indicating how these standards were to be met. The standards cover most of the major rivers and streams in the country, and are enforceable by Federal abatement actions. State enforcement of the standards, given impetus by the threat of Federal action, gives good grounds for believing that the 1965 act will form a sound basis for a significant reduction of water pollution. Not only is there the threat of Federal intervention, but the fact that all states have federally approved standards reduces the risk that a state or locality will retard industrial development by actively controlling pollution. Such risk has been a major impediment to state and local pollution control in the past.

RESPONSIBILITY FOR AIR POLLUTION CONTROL

Until quite recently the interest of most state governments in controlling air pollution was minimal or nonexistent. Insofar as control efforts were made they were made by local government, usually in the large cities where the problem was most acute. The first state air pollution act authorizing enforcement at the state level was passed by Oregon in 1952, and only eighteen states had passed legislation before 1963.[10]

The lack of state interest in air pollution was due in part to the problem being considered nothing more than an unaesthetic nuisance. It was also due to the more localized nature of air pollution compared with water pollution. In one sense air pollution is the least localized of problems, because air flows freely and knows no terrestrial boundaries. But in a sense which is more meaningful from the standpoint of abatement action, air pollution, with the exception of pollution from motor vehicles, is highly localized. The problem arises from a large number of stationary sources, and if it is to be corrected it must be corrected at each of these sources. It cannot be centrally collected and treated like water pollution. The local nature of air pollution was even more apparent before the role of the automobile was realized and before communities considered the imposition of general restrictions on the use of certain types of fuel.

TABLE 6–2. **State Air Pollution Control**

State	1. Agency	2. 1967 Budget (in $000; incl. Fed. grants)	3. 1967 Personnel (in man-years)	4. Date of First AP Act	5. Date of Current Act
Ala.	Board of Health	50	7	1969	1969
Alaska	Dept. of Health & Welfare	0	0	1959	1959
Ariz.	Dept. of Health	0	0	1962	1967
Ark.	Pollution Control Comm'n.	58	7	1965	1965
Calif.	Dept. of Public Health	2,407	102*	1947	1968
Colo.	Board of Health	118	10	1963	1966
Conn.	Health Dept.	152	17	1967	1967
Del.	Board of Health	0	0	1957	1966
Fla.	Board of Health	175*	15*	1957	1967
Ga.	Dept. of Public Health	49	8	1967	1967
Hawaii	Dept. of Health	76	6	1957	1957
Idaho	Board of Health	27	3	1959	1967
Ill.	Dept. of Public Health	156	15	1963	1963
Ind.	Board of Health	82	9	1961	1961
Iowa	Dept. of Health	0	0	1967	1967
Kan.	Dept. of Health	0	0	1967	1967
Ky.	Dept. of Health	317	27	1952	1968
La.	Air Control Comm'n.	103	9	1964	1964
Maine	Dept. of Health & Welfare	0	0	1969	1969

State	1. Agency	2. 1967 Budget (in $000; incl. Fed. grants)	3. 1967 Personnel (in man-years)	4. Date of First AP Act	5. Date of Current Act
Md.	Board of Health & Mental Hygiene	95	9	1963	1967
Mass.	Dept. of Public Health	11	1	1954	1963
Mich.	Health Dept.	147	12	1965	1965
Minn.	Board of Health	0	0	1957	1967
Miss.	Air & Water Pollution Control Comm'n.	0	0	1966	1966
Mo.	Air Conservation Comm'n.	108	7	1965	1965
Mont.	Board of Health	47	3	1967	1967
Nebr.	Dept. of Health	0	0	1969	1969
Nev.	Division of Envt'l Health	0	0	1967	1967
N.H.	Dept. of Health & Welfare	31	2	1967	1967
N.J.	Dept. of Health	808	69	1954	1967
N.M.	Dept. of Pub. Health	13	3	1967	1967
N.Y.	Air Pollution Control Board	2,371	50*	1957	1966
N.C.	Dept. of Public Health	0	0	1963	1967
N.D.	Dept. of Health	0	2	1969	1969
Ohio	Dept. of Health	128	8	1957	1967
Okla.	Dept. of Health	10	1	1965	1967
Ore.	Board of Health	187	15	1961	1961
Pa.	Dept. of Health	369	44	1960	1966
R.I.	Dept. of Health	10	2	1966	1966
S.C.	Pollution Control Authority	71	5	1963	1965
S.D.	Dept. of Health	0	0	1970	1970
Tenn.	Dept. of Public Health	13	3	1959	1967
Tex.	Air Control Board	108	10	1965	1967
Utah	Dept. of Public Health	39	3	1967	1967
Vt.	Health Dept.	0	0	1968	1968
Va.	Air Pollution Control Board	25	2	1966	1966
Wash.	Dept. of Health	115	8	1957	1967
W.Va.	Air Pollution Control Comm'n.	254	27	1961	1967
Wisc.	Board of Health	0	0	1967	1967
Wyo.	Board of Health	8	0	1967	1967
Total		8,738	521	----	----
Median		43	3	1964	1967

Sources: Cols. 1, 2, and 3: U.S. Senate, Com. on Public Works, "Air Pollution—1967" pt. 3, pp. 1160–1283; Cols. 4 and 5: *ibid.*; HEW, PHS, "A Digest of State Air Pollution Laws, 1967 ed." (Washington, D.C.: GPO, 1968); and *Journal of the Air Pollution Control Association,* "legislative notes," various issues.

*Estimated

NOTE: Due to discrepancies in state reporting and differences in interpretation, the information, especially the dates in columns 4 and 5, may not be precisely comparable with state or Federal figures. Dates in column 5 are as of mid-1968, with the exception of states which have passed their first law since then.

Before 1950, air pollution control at the local level was directed almost exclusively at the problem of smoke. Several communities, notably Pittsburgh, achieved considerable success in reducing the amount of smoke emitted into the local atmosphere. The Pittsburgh drive on air pollution started in 1946 with a decision by financier Richard Mellon to renew the declining industrial city. The heavy pall which had given Pittsburgh the nickname of "The Smoky City" was obviously one of the major factors inhibiting new development. Mellon, with the cooperation of Mayor David Lawrence, launched a vigorous control effort which succeeded in sharply reducing the amount of smoke and soot coming from the stacks of the city's heavy industry.[11] However, the limited nature of the city's accomplishments is indicated by the fact that in 1967 the Public Health Service still listed Pittsburgh as the sixth most polluted city in the nation.[12]

Despite the more localized characteristics of air pollution, the same difficulties that local control experienced in water pollution began to be encountered in the air pollution control effort. The lines of political jurisdiction did not coincide with the flow of dirty air, and control efforts in one community were frustrated by the lack of controls in neighboring communities. However, the fact that air pollution was confined primarily to urban areas made the states less willing to assume responsibility than they had been for water pollution. There was thus a shift of responsibility not to the state level but to the county or regional level. This shift began in the early 1950's, and by 1965 half of all local programs had jurisdiction over an entire county or several counties.[13]

The growing realization of the health effects of air pollution has led to local governments increasingly placing responsibility for air pollution control in the local health department. Originally the control function in many communities was the responsibility of the buildings department because of the emphasis placed on inspection of boilers. By 1965 more than half of the local air pollution agencies were located in the health department, only 10 per cent were in the buildings department, and the remainder were either independent or under some other department. Over 80 per cent of the agencies created between 1961 and 1965 were placed in the health department.[14] This is in marked contrast to the trend in water pollution, where jurisdiction has been increasingly taken away from health officials. At the state level, thirty-seven of the states vest air pollution control authority in the state health department. Only six states have created separate units to deal with both air and water pollution.[15]

In 1967, with the introduction and passage of the Air Quality Act, a great shift began in the locus of air pollution control efforts. The primary responsibility up to this point had rested with local governments. But the threat of large-scale Federal intervention and the responsibility for standard-setting placed on the states by the new legislation stimulated the states to take action. During 1967 twenty state legislatures enacted comprehensive air pollution control laws, and six other states adopted amendments to strengthen earlier legislation.[16] In 1963 only three states (California, New Jersey, and New York) had air pollution budgets exceeding $100,000. By the end of 1967, twenty-two states had budgets over $100,000.[17]

Despite the great increase in state effort, with a few exceptions the states are clearly not ready to perform the tasks demanded of them under the 1967 act. A look at Table 6-2 quickly reveals the inadequacy of most of the state programs, in terms of budgets and personnel. The primary initial task of the states will be to establish standards for the air quality control regions within their jurisdiction. These standards will be for the most difficult types of pollutants, technically and politically, and will cover the most urbanized parts of the state. But a majority of the states have not established any standards for any part of the state. This lack of state experience in standard-setting is quite different from the situation which prevailed in water pollution at the time the 1965 Water Quality Act was passed. In water pollution, state responsibility for the problem was well established, and almost every state had had considerable experience in the setting of standards.

In any air pollution control program there are three basic steps. The first is the monitoring of air quality and the inventorying of emission sources; the second is the establishment of standards; and the third is the enforcement of those standards. About half the states undertake monitoring activities, usually in cooperation with the monitoring network established by NAPCA. The monitoring, however, is usually quite inadequate, with only one or two sampling stations for the entire state. For example, New Jersey, one of the more advanced states, had, until 1968, only one location in which air quality was measured. A few of the major metropolitan areas are now beginning to install adequate air sampling systems. New York City, for example, began in 1968 to supplement its lone sampling station by placing monitoring equipment in twenty different locations throughout the city. Very few cities and no states have completed emission inventories.

We have already discussed the inadequacy of standard-setting efforts. In addition to the eight or ten states which have undertaken significant regulatory activity, a few of the larger cities have also established fairly comprehensive standards. In most cases, however, the localities have lacked the technical know-how to undertake the setting of standards.

Enforcement activity has not necessarily been a function of standard-setting. Those localities which have active air pollution control programs have proceeded to try to control pollution sources using their police power and their authority to abate nuisances. They have responded to citizen complaints and have attacked the most obvious problems first. As the director of air pollution control in one industrial community put it, "It was strictly an eyeball confrontation at the onset. No emissions or air quality standards were necessary to get our industries on the road to controlling their pollution. It was too serious and obvious a problem to be denied or toyed with." [18] Many communities, probably a majority of those with any air pollution control activities, are still concerned exclusively with smoke control. The obvious and visible nature of smoke pollution makes the lack of standards less of a handicap.

COMPLIANCE AT THE STATE AND LOCAL LEVEL

The existence of numerous local governments, each jealously guarding its prerogatives and each diligently ignoring or working at cross-purposes with its neighboring governments, is one of the major underlying problems of the American polity. The problems posed by pollution accentuate this pattern and reveal some of its adverse consequences.

The classic conflict in water pollution is between the upstream polluter and the downstream victim of pollution. The upstream community receives all the benefits of being able to use the river as a sewer but pays none of the costs of pollution. The downstream victim receives none of the benefits but pays all the costs of dirty water. The limited jurisdiction of the local governments thus creates a disincentive to take any action to control pollution. The same disparity between who bears the costs and who gains the benefits exists in almost all metropolitan areas with respect to air pollution.

The effect of the "externalities" caused by the flow of air and water are reinforced by the rivalry among communities for industrial ratables. In most communities the desire for clean air and water is weighed against the fear of losing out in the race to attract new business and industry and to retain the industries which have already located in the town. If a community sets more stringent control standards than its neighbors, the plant looking for a new location may choose one of the neighbors to avoid the cost of installing control equipment. Thus this rivalry creates a further incentive for lenient standards and lax enforcement.

Data are not available to indicate the actual effects of pollution regulations on plant location or relocation. Local officials probably exaggerate the impact which such regulations have, but industry groups do take advantage of the rivalry of local communities and the fragmentation of metropolitan areas. Where industry has already established its own enclaves within a metropolis, the industrial community is unlikely to do much in the way of controlling pollution, and will be reluctant to disturb the status quo. A state air pollution official in Missouri observed that

... in the Kansas City area, which is smaller and more homogeneous than the St. Louis area, and where there are fewer of what might be called special purpose municipalities, the industrial community has supported the formation of a regional authority, whereas in the St. Louis area where little industrial villages abound, industry has maintained a silence on the subject, which one can only regard as hostile.[19]

The lack of cooperation among local governments interferes with sound planning for the installation of sewers and treatment plants, and results in the wastage of large amounts of funds for such facilities.[20] Individual communities build separate treatment plants when a combined plant would be far more efficient, suburbanites invest in individual septic tanks which must then be replaced by sewers and a treatment plant, towns build facilities which rapidly become obsolete because sufficient allowance has not been made for population growth. The obstacles to pollution control are compounded by a failure to work together and to plan.[21]

The state-local compliance process is characterized by negotiation, as is the Federal process. The Federal government negotiates primarily with the state control agencies, but the state and local control agencies in their turn must carry out negotiations with the polluters. Matthew Holden, Jr., summarizes the state-local situation when he says:

> In reality, regulatory decision-makers will not usually have this ability to ordain, because the parties who must comply have sufficient ability to "filibuster" that the agency loses much of its potentiality for success. Successful regulation thus depends on the consent of the regulated. Such consent is achieved by a process of bargaining—both explicit and tacit—which induces the regulated parties to agree (even reluctantly) to that which the regulator proposes.[22]

There are numerous opportunities for polluters to "filibuster" during the steps which lead to compliance. They may take steps to weaken the pollution control agency or deprive it of necessary powers. They may try to have the agency or the legislature set lenient or unenforceable quality standards. They may try to prevent quality standards from being translated into emission standards or fight to prevent the emission standards from being too stringent. When a case is brought against a specific polluter, he can negotiate with the control agency about the nature of the remedial measures he must take and the length of time allowed for compliance. If negotiations with the control agency are unsatisfactory, the polluter can go to court where a good lawyer will be able to delay any effective action for several years.[23]

There are a number of factors which influence the effectiveness of a state or local control agency in getting polluters to comply with established standards. Obviously the resources and competence of the control agency itself will be crucial. The availability of technologically feasible means for controlling the pollution form another limiting factor. However, the economic and political characteristics of the polluter and the legal and public relations aspects of the control program will also significantly influence the final outcome. We have already discussed some of these factors in relation to industrial polluters.[24]

The range of tactics and the political muscle available to the polluter are often crucial determinants of the pace and ultimate outcome of compliance efforts. The threat to move or close down is a useful political tactic, especially in communities heavily dependent on the polluting industry. The cases in which it is most difficult to achieve compliance are those where an industry or firm is economically marginal and politically influential. E. F. Murphy, illustrating this point, cites the case of the Wisconsin dairy industry which consists of a large number of small firms who, banded together, exercise considerable political influence.[25]

Municipal governments are often among the most flagrant violators of both air and water pollution standards. Their failure to construct adequate sewage treatment facilities or to place proper controls on municipal incinerators contributes significantly to the pollution problem. While most municipalities must be credited with good intentions concerning pollution control, compliance is made difficult because they fall into the category noted above of being hard-pressed for funds but politically influential. Most local budgets are very tight, but it is difficult to force the local government to take action because it has influence with the Governor and the state legislature.

The ultimate sanction of the pollution control agency is court action. For this sanction to be credible and to have the necessary warning effect on actual or potential polluters, the cooperation of the courts is necessary. If the polluters actually taken to court are let off with admonishments or inconsequential fines, then the control agency is deprived of one of its major weapons. It is left without any final sanction to enforce its rulings. The action of the courts has been a major handicap to pollution control in many cities and states. Major firms have been fined $25 for violating air pollution codes or have been given no penalty at all. In some cases court interpretation of pollution statutes has been extremely narrow and limiting.[26]

The use of publicity to force polluters to comply with regulations can often be an effective technique. The major limitation here is the inability of the public to understand the complicated negotiations which may take place between the control agency and the polluter, and the reluctance or inability of the agency to publicize such negotiations. The public sees and comprehends the broad statements of policy issued by the agency, but the actual decisions made by the agency on individual polluters tend to be technical and little publicized. Such decisions are, however, the key to the success of any pollution control program.[27]

INTERSTATE ACTIVITIES IN AIR AND WATER POLLUTION CONTROL

Air pollution and water pollution are both classic examples of problems which defy political boundaries.[28] Water pollution is a river basin problem, and almost all the major rivers in the United States cross state boundaries. Air pollution is an "airshed" problem. Nobody has been able to give a satisfactory definition of the extent of an airshed, but it is clear that air pollution is concentrated in the nation's metropolitan areas and more than a third of the metropolitan area population lives in areas which straddle state lines.[29] Thus one of the major problems in controlling pollution is the difficulty of striking a balance between the regional scope of the problem and the state-centered sources of power capable of taking action.

The states suffer from the same problems of rivalry and lack of cooperation as the localities. State governments do not like to surrender power. The reluctance to impose stringent pollution controls for fear of hindering economic development is as much a factor in state thinking as in local calculations. The difficulty of the states getting together has resulted in limited, and on the whole, disappointing experience with interstate cooperation for pollution control.

In the water pollution field there are five interstate compact agencies which are sufficiently active to qualify for Federal grants—the New England Interstate Water Pollution Control Commission, the Interstate Commission on the Potomac River Basin, the Interstate Sanitation Commission (New York, New Jersey, and Connecticut), the Ohio River Valley Water Sanitation Commission, and the Delaware River Basin Commission. The New England and Potomac commissions have very few powers and generally do little more than provide minimal coordination for the work of the member states. The New England Commission consists of five commissioners from each of the member states (Connecticut, Maine, Massachusetts, New Hampshire, New York, Rhode Island, and Vermont). It conducts some research, training, and public information programs, and gives technical advice to the states on construction of treatment plants and legislation. It has no enforcement authority. Its major function is the establishment of standards through the classification of interstate waters. The standard-setting function amounts to a rubber-stamp approval of the standards submitted by the separate states, since each state takes the initiative in establishing the classification for waters within its boundaries and a majority of the commissioners from a state can veto any action of the commission which affects their state.[30] The Potomac Commission is equally weak, despite the fact that it includes a Federal representative.

The Ohio River Valley Water Sanitation Commission, better known as ORSANCO, has frequently been cited as one of the examples of a successful interstate commission.[31] ORSANCO began operating in 1948. It consists of three representatives from the Federal government and three representatives from each of the eight member states—Ohio, West Virginia, Illinois, Indiana, Kentucky, New York, Virginia, and Pennsylvania. The commission has authority to issue enforcement orders and bring polluters to court, but it has exercised its enforcement power only six times in the course of eighteen years, and in none of these instances has the case gone to court. Defenders of ORSANCO attribute this to the success which the commission has had in voluntarily persuading municipalities and industries to clean up their pollution. However, the limited use of ORSANCO's legal power may also be due to the fact that enforcement action can be taken only if a majority of the commissioners from a majority of the member states agree, and then only if a majority of the commissioners from the state from which the pollution originates assent. This requirement makes it politically almost impossible for the commission to use its enforcement authority. In recognition of this limitation, ORSANCO has taken on the role of coordinating and supplementing the state programs rather than trying to exercise complete control over pollution in the Ohio Basin.[32]

The only valid measure of ORSANCO's success or failure is the degree to which pollution has actually been controlled in the Ohio River, but even on this basis it is not easy to draw any clear-cut conclusions. In 1948, the sewage of less than 38 per cent of the population in the basin was treated; by 1966, 94 per cent of the population was covered by treatment facilities. In 1953, only 323 of the 1,247 industrial plants in the area covered by the commission had adequate pollution control facilities; by 1966, the number of plants in the area had increased to 1,769, of which 1,569 had installed control facilities meeting the commission's minimum requirements.[33] However, the commission has required only primary treatment of wastes whereas the Federal government has declared that secondary treatment is necessary to meet the pollution problem. Most observers agree that the Ohio is still a very polluted river, and it has been reported that the Federal government is considering initiating Federal enforcement action to clean it up.[34] While impressive progress has been made under the aegis of ORSANCO, it seems clear that the commission cannot be considered an unqualified success.

The Interstate Sanitation Commission has jurisdiction over the New York metropolitan region. Its powers are similar to those possessed by ORSANCO, and it has pursued the same strategy of voluntary cooperation as the Ohio Commission, with about the same mixed results. Although the New York area still suffers from a high degree of pollution, the ISC has made an important contribution in prodding municipalities and industries to invest in control facilities. In 1961 the ISC was authorized to monitor air pollution in the New York region. The member states have pushed for the commission to assume the full range of air pollution standard-setting and enforcement activities in response to the Federal demand for a regional air pollution authority, but HEW has considered the ISC too weak a body to undertake such activities.

The Delaware River Basin Commission (DRBC) is among the newest of the interstate commissions, and it is unique in the scope of its powers. It was formed in 1961 by agreement of the Federal government and the states of New York, New Jersey, Pennsylvania, and Delaware.[35] Each state is represented on the commission by its Governor, and the Secretary of the Interior serves as the Federal representative.

The DRBC is responsible for all aspects of water resource development in the basin, not just for pollution control. The commission has adopted a basin-wide comprehensive plan, which includes provisions for water supply, pollution control, flood protection, and recreation; and it has a wide range of powers to implement programs in these areas, including authority to construct treatment works and other water development projects and to enforce pollution control regulations.

Up to now the DRBC has not exercised its full authority to control water pollution. Between 1961 and 1965, the commission and FWPCA cooperated in a comprehensive study of the basin;[36] between 1965 and 1968, the commission was engaged in formulating and approving detailed water quality standards and regulations based on the findings of the comprehensive study. The final regulations adopted by the commission in March 1968 require that the daily oxygen demand of discharged wastes be reduced from their present level of 1,000,000 pounds to 322,000 pounds. This will mean installation of secondary treatment by all industrial and municipal sources at an estimated cost of $500 million.[37] Compliance with this ambitious goal was originally scheduled for 1972, but the cutbacks in Federal waste treatment grants will probably retard the implementation schedule. If the commission accomplishes its

goal within a reasonable period of time it will be an outstanding exception to the otherwise mixed performance of interstate
compact organizations.

No interstate agencies to control air pollution have been
approved by the Congress. In 1968, congressional hearings
were held on three interstate compacts, but the results amounted
to a veto of all of the compacts. The three interstate agreements considered by Congress were: (1) The Indiana-Illinois
compact; (2) the Ohio--West Virginia compact; and (3) the Mid-
Atlantic States compact, which had been ratified by New York,
New Jersey, and Connecticut, and which also provided for
Pennsylvania and Delaware to join. The Indiana-Illinois compact was submitted to Congress in 1965. The other two compacts
were submitted in 1967, having been rather hastily drawn up
to avoid anticipated Federal intervention under the 1967
Air Quality Act.

The Indiana-Illinois compact languished in Congress for
three years because of doubts on the part of both HEW and
some key congressmen that it would be effective in controlling
pollution. The compact was modeled on the ORSANCO
agreement[38] and retained the veto power of the polluting state
which, as noted above, has limited the use ORSANCO has
made of its enforcement power. The commission which would
have been established under the compact would not have contained any representative of the Federal government, an omission to which HEW strongly objected when a similar proposal
was made by New York and New Jersey. The wording of the
Indiana-Illinois compact also left some doubt as to the proposed commission's authority to set adequate air pollution
control standards.[39]

All three proposed compacts were questioned on the grounds
of their compatibility with the 1967 Air Quality Act. The act
provides that the Secretary of HEW must, by May 21, 1969,
establish "air quality control regions" which will serve as the
basis for setting and enforcing air quality standards. It states
that

It is the intent of Congress that no agreement or compact entered
into between states after the date of enactment of the Air Quality

Act of 1967, which relates to the control and abatement of air pollution in an air quality control region, shall provide for participation by a state which is not included (in whole or in part) in such air quality control region.[40]

Although the Mid-Atlantic compact was approved by New York and New Jersey before the Air Quality Act was passed, the proposed inclusion of Delaware and Pennsylvania clearly seemed to violate the intent of the act.

On June 17, 1968, the Senate Committee on Public Works, to whom the three proposed interstate compacts had been referred by the Senate Judiciary Committee, issued its report on the compacts.[41] Although the committee's formal recommendation was that the compacts be approved, it attached so many conditions to such approval that the real effect of the report was one of disapproval. The committee's conditions would have made it necessary for the compacts to be redrafted and then, presumably, reratified by each of the member states, before congressional approval was given.

The action of the Public Works Committee was sufficient to kill the Mid-Atlantic and probably the Indiana-Illinois compacts. However, the Ohio–West Virginia compact was strengthened and revised to conform to the Air Quality Act, was passed by both state legislatures in its revised form, and submitted to Congress in July 1969. There is a good chance that it will be approved by Congress in 1970.

The relationship between interstate compacts and air quality control regions has not been made clear by HEW, and it will probably not become clear until there have been several years of experimentation. HEW has stated:

> Interstate compacts are not mandatory under the Air Quality Act of 1967, but they are one potentially useful means of providing for cooperation among states in meeting responsibilities placed on them. Since they provide a statutory basis for interstate cooperation and since they can also be the foundation for a single comprehensive approach to an air pollution problem involving a number of jurisdictions, they have many advantages over other possible arrangements for cooperative action.[42]

What remain unclear are the answers to such questions as

whether an interstate compact should cover more than one air quality control region, how existing interstate commissions would relate to the interstate air quality agencies provided for in the act, and how interstate commissions would function in relation to the state-oriented standard-setting process established by the act.

The Air Quality Act authorizes HEW to pay for two years up to 100 per cent of the air quality planning program costs of any interstate agency designated by the governors of the affected states. After this initial period, grants are authorized for up to three-fourths of such costs. The purpose of the HEW grant is to expedite the establishment of air quality standards in an interstate air quality control region by having the interstate agency recommend proposed standards to the affected governors. If the states fail to take action to establish their own interstate agency, the Secretary of HEW can establish an interstate air quality planning commission, chaired and staffed by HEW, for the purpose of assisting the Secretary in establishing standards. These provisions give strong impetus to the states to join in cooperative action, but they also allow for wide leeway in determining the form this cooperative action will take.

The sections of the Air Quality Act relating to interstate cooperation would seem to place adequate emphasis on interstate agencies even though the act's standard-setting provisions are based on individual states. The 1965 Water Quality Act, which provided for the same standard-setting procedure as the Air Quality Act, did not deal at all with the setting of standards within the jurisdiction of interstate agencies. Agencies like ORSANCO were threatened with splits among the member states, each of which submitted its own standards and negotiated individually with the Interior Department. However, in the case of the Delaware River Basin Commission, Interior chose to strengthen the commission by giving its standards priority over those of the member states. Interior Secretary Udall said: "The standards adopted by the Commission last year are critical to my review and approval of standards for the Basin. While not formally approved [because under the law there was no way for them to be approved], they serve as our model for the Basin and I am insisting that standards submitted by each of the states be consistent with those adopted by the Commission for the Basin."[43] Presumably HEW will treat the standards developed by the interstate agencies established pursuant to the 1967 act in much the same way that Interior treated the DRBC standards, although one can imagine some politically difficult situations arising in cases where a Governor of a member state submits standards which are not consistent with those of an interstate agency.

One of the major unsettled questions concerning interstate agencies is the form which Federal representation should take. In the absence of Federal representation, the compact commissions tend to compromise decisions to the lowest common denominator in order to get agreement among the member states, and the strength of the commission is thus reduced to that of the weakest partner. On the other hand, if there is a Federal voting member on the commission, later review of the commission's decisions by the Federal government will be difficult because the Federal representative will already have taken a stand. For example, if the Federal member of the DRBC, who is the Secretary of the Interior, votes for certain water quality standards it will be difficult for him later to disapprove those standards. HEW has taken the position that interstate commissions should have Federal representation but that the Federal members should not vote.[44] Experience with interstate compacts has really been too meager to determine whether this is the most desirable approach.

INTERGOVERNMENTAL RELATIONS

Federal representation on interstate commissions is only one of the many forms of interaction among the different levels of government involved in pollution control. Like all other governmental activities in America, control of air and water pollution does not break down into a neat and sharply defined division of labor between state, local, and Federal government.[45] Functions are shared and tasks carried out by cooperative interaction between the different levels.

Responsibility for pollution control has followed a progression to higher levels of government. We have seen how both air and water pollution were originally the responsibilities of local government. Water pollution became increasingly a state responsibility in the late nineteenth and early twentieth century, and then, following World War II, the Federal government assumed increasing authority. Control of air pollution has been progressing from the local to the state and regional level with the Federal government playing an even larger role. It is not difficult to foresee, within the coming years, the growth of international cooperation and perhaps international authority in the vital task of preserving the environment.

The expanding role of higher levels of government has been due to the increasing geographical spread and the growing acuteness of the pollution problem, combined with the inadequate efforts of lower levels of government to enforce controls. It has been fostered by the general growth of ever larger public and private networks of power and by the development of administrative techniques to control large organizations and to deal with complex problems. Pollution control has thus been a part of the general twentieth-century trend toward increasing the scope of government in general and the higher levels of government in particular.

It should not be assumed that the increasing role of the Federal government has been at the expense of state or local power, however. The states probably have lost some power to the Federal government in the water pollution field, but the increasing authority of Washington is offset by two factors. First, each state never did possess the power to control pollution coming from outside its borders, and thus the Federal responsibility for truly interstate pollution does not come at any government's expense. This is even clearer if we look at the state's assumption of local responsibility for water pollution control. During the nineteenth century the localities may theoretically have held the responsibility for controlling pollution, but they never had the power or ability to fulfill that responsibility. Thus the takeover by the state was not really a loss of power for the localities. Second, the increased Federal role may actually result in greater power and authority at the state level. This is certainly the case for air pollution, where the Air Quality Act has stimulated states to take on authority and responsibility which they never had before. The same is true, although to a lesser extent, of the effect of the 1965 Water Quality Act.

Cooperation is the dominant mode in intergovernmental relations. The daily work of controlling pollution is in the hands of professional personnel who share a common dedication to getting the job done. This dedication is constantly reinforced by professional conferences, training programs, and informal contacts. The overlap of responsibilities results in frequent interaction among the different levels and it is not uncommon for engineers, chemists, and other professionals to have had experience working for local, state, and Federal agencies. A former commissioner of FWPCA had previously been the chief of the Texas water pollution control agency, and the current chief of New York City's Department of Air Pollution Control was formerly in charge of one of the Federal government's regional offices. Many similar examples could be cited. Money and technical assistance from the higher levels to the lower help to keep the system operating smoothly.

While cooperation is the norm in Federal-state-local interaction, conflict is not uncommon, as we have seen. Different constituencies, traditions, styles, and perspectives make some friction inevitable. Conflict between political officials at different levels is more common than between professionals, but the professionals have their share of problems and resentments. For example, Frank Graham quotes a PHS official talking about Federal enforcement actions who says that it is obvious that state officials assume Federal intervention to be an attack on their professional reputations. "It looks like a reflection on the job they're doing, and, frankly, it is."[46]

What Morton Grodzins has called the "multiple crack" aspect of American federalism, whereby if an interest loses on one level it can fight on another, plays a significant part in pollution control. Thus the coal and oil industry, having lost the fight over Federal regulations on sulfur dioxide air pollution, carried the battle to the state and local level. But it is not only the polluters who get multiple cracks. State and local groups urging stronger controls against pollution have often urged Federal action if, in the view of such groups, the states and localities have not shown vigor in prosecuting polluters.

The ability of groups to pursue their interest at different levels does not negate the fact that particular interests consistently receive a more sympathetic hearing at certain levels. We have already noted the greater influence of industrial groups at the state and local level than at the Federal. This process tends to be self-reinforcing. Thus, industry's preference for state action has led it to write and lobby for interstate air pollution compacts instead of Federal action. The influence of industry groups in formulating the compacts enables them to structure such compacts in their favor, and also wins them the gratitude of state officials; this in turn strengthens still further industry influence at the state level.

We have described the complex of factors and attitudes which play a part in the politics of pollution. The interaction between the many different groups becomes clearer if we examine their roles in the major aspects of pollution control. Thus we turn next to the major problems which concern those who have an interest in controlling pollution—research, standard-setting, and compliance.

Part III

THE POLICY PROCESS

CHAPTER 7

Research and Standard-setting

IT HAS FREQUENTLY been stated that pollution can be brought under control with existing technology, that what is needed to obtain clean air and water is not research but money and political muscle. There is much truth in such statements—the major part of pollution in the United States can be eliminated by applying existing scientific knowledge. But there is also much about the effects of pollution and how to control them which is not known and which needs to be known. This is partially evidenced by the fact that about half the budget of both NAPCA and FWPCA (excluding waste treatment grants) is devoted to research of one kind or another.

There are two basic areas of research in the pollution field. The first is concerned with discovering the effects of pollution. Although man has been making major changes in the natural order for at least a hundred years, we are still remarkably ignorant about the effects of such changes on natural processes or on human beings. We do not know whether the many chemicals which man dumps into the air, water, and soil are injurious to health. There are good grounds for believing that some of them are, but we do not know how much of which ones are injurious. We do not know whether the burning of fossil fuels is producing irreversible changes in the composition of the earth's atmosphere and, if it is, what the ramifications of such changes are. When we build dams, drain swamps, or irrigate large areas we do not know the full effects of such projects on water, soil, fish, or wildlife.

It is necessary to know the effects of pollution if one is to formulate a rational program of control. Until we know the effects of a pollutant it is difficult to determine whether it should be controlled and, if so, how stringent the controls should be. If, in fact, emissions from the burning of fuel are permanently changing the amount of carbon dioxide in the atmosphere, and if such a change will result in an increase in world temperature, the melting of the polar ice caps, and consequent flooding on a massive scale, then clearly extraordinary efforts are warranted in controlling such emissions. If, on the other hand, such a chain of events is not likely, and if, in addition, the health effects of low levels of carbon dioxide are discovered to be insignificant, then control of carbon dioxide emissions becomes a low-priority matter.

The second area of pollution research is concerned with methods of controlling particular kinds or sources of pollutants. In water pollution we still do not know of practical ways of preventing the eutrophication of lakes or the runoff of sediment and chemicals into rivers. In air pollution adequate and economical control techniques are lacking for many major pollutants. In several areas of both air and water pollution, methods of control are available but the financial or political costs of applying them make searches for alternative methods necessary. All of the combined sewers in the country could be ripped out and replaced with separate storm and sanitary sewers; the burning of low-sulfur instead of high-sulfur fuels could be substituted in all urban areas; but in both these cases the costs of such moves have been judged by many to exceed the benefits and much effort has been expended in the search for other control methods.

The factors which determine the allocation of research funds and the setting of priorities among research projects are complex. To some extent the priorities are set by the working scientists. Their evaluation of what problems or approaches are interesting or important will go far in determining the work done in the laboratories. However, the politicians and the program administrators not only decide on the total amount of funds available for research but also have an important say in establishing priorities.

Some areas of research are promoted primarily because of political considerations. For example, the key positions on the relevant congressional committees held by representatives from Eastern coal-mining states has led to a series of major research projects on the control of air pollution from burning piles of coal mine wastes. Some areas of research are initiated and defended primarily by the scientists working on them. Much of FWPCA's research has been devoted to the development of advanced methods of waste treatment, methods which will remove more impurities than the techniques currently in use. While the projects on advanced waste treatment have received congressional and Executive Branch support, their primary backers have been the scientists within FWPCA.

Probably the most common pattern is for the influence of scientists, administrators, or politicians to be almost inextricably intertwined in the determination of research activities. The current research priority for NAPCA is the development of control methods for sulfur oxides pollution. The ranking of sulfur oxides as a major health hazard was a decision of the air pollution scientists. But the political repercussions of curbing the use of high-sulfur coal and oil led Congress and the Executive Branch to push for research on control technology.[1] Once the emphasis on control technology was established, however, initiative returned to the scientists as to which control techniques would be most fruitful. Yet even in deciding among alternative techniques, the judgment of the scientists was modified by factors of interagency rivalry, with the Department of the Interior advocating certain approaches and HEW others. Thus the pattern of actual research projects was a result of complex interaction involving interest group pressure, scientific findings, congressional and Executive political sensitivities, and interagency conflicts.

The degree to which research projects are controlled and supervised by government personnel is determined primarily by whether the projects are undertaken "in-house," as it is termed, or through grants or contracts. In-house research is research done by government scientists in government laboratories. Research grants are given to individuals or institutions for projects chosen and developed by the applicants for such grants. Research contracts are awarded to educational institutions or private firms for carrying out projects selected by the government.

The major advantage of in-house research is that it enables the officials of an agency to exercise a high degree of supervision and thus to ensure that the research will be relevant to the problems the agency wants solved. Once an agency has built up a capability for doing its own research, it also acquires a certain degree of flexibility in pursuing research topics. It can investigate ideas which are simply hunches or which are still in a formative stage. On the other hand, the existence of such a capability creates an obvious pressure to make use of it, and thus the agency loses flexibility as to how much research it wants to undertake and whether it wants it done within the agency or in the private sector.

Obtaining competent personnel is one of the major limitations on in-house research. Government salaries for almost all types of scientists are significantly below those offered by educational institutions and private industry. While security, fringe benefits, or draft exemption may lure some scientists, government recruitment efforts are forced to rely primarily on the scientist's dedication to the public welfare. A less well recognized problem, but one which is becoming acute with the undertaking of large-scale, complex research projects, is the skill required to plan directed research. Modern, sophisticated administrative techniques are necessary for the successful planning and conduct of multi-million-dollar projects directed at producing specific outcomes; but, outside of the Defense Department, administrators who can apply such techniques are extremely scarce within the Federal government. Finally, in-house research is at the mercy of political factors. Funds may be reduced with little warning, supervisors may suddenly be shifted to some other post, new laboratories may be created, thus scattering competent research personnel. Such problems also occur in the private sector, but they seem to happen with greater frequency in government.

Research grants are designed as much to promote interest in some topic and thereby recruit scientific personnel as they are to produce worthwhile research findings. The grants are usually small, whereas the problems to be solved usually require a major effort. Although most agencies make some effort to award grants on the basis of the agency's own ranking of research priorities, coordination between agency objectives and the topics of research grants is often tenuous. Supervision of the research done under grants is almost nonexistent and it is not unusual for the grant project to follow a path quite different from that outlined in the grant application. Research grants are most useful in areas which are scientifically "under-developed," as air pollution was up to a few years ago. However, as a way of obtaining scientific findings, the value of research grants diminishes as the parameters of a problem become better known.

Partly as a result of the shortcomings of in-house research and research grants, the use of research contracts has increased significantly in recent years throughout the government and in the area of pollution control. Contracts enable a government agency to choose the institution best capable of undertaking a particular project. The agency does not have to create a competence in a particular area but can simply utilize the manpower and equipment already acquired in the private sector. The contract can spell out in detail precisely what the research should produce. As pollution research has moved increasingly toward seeking specific control techniques for specific problems, the contract approach has become more and more useful.

Many of the contracts in pollution control are made with private industry, and fears have often been raised that the outcome of some research may be biased by the interests of a particular industry. Many members of Congress and the Executive Branch exhibit a rather schizophrenic attitude, on the one hand urging that industry become more involved in pollution research and on the other recoiling in horror when government research monies are entrusted to private hands. Up to this point it is hard to find any examples of government contracts in the pollution area being abused or subverted because of private bias. The advantages obtained from involving industry have probably far exceeded the dangers of such involvement. But the stake which industry has in government research and its ability to influence the nature and direction of such research should not be underestimated.

The Federal government's consideration of whether to undertake a study of an electric or battery-powered automobile provides an excellent example of the stake industry can have in government research. A number of air pollution experts have predicted that in twenty or thirty years' time the increase in the number of automobiles will overtake improvements in emission control systems and that pollution from gasoline-powered vehicles will become progressively worse. The conclusion drawn from this is that there will have to be a major effort to replace gasoline with some nonpolluting fuel source, such as electricity. For several years bills were introduced in both the House and the Senate calling for government-sponsored research on nonpolluting vehicles. In 1966, the Senate Commerce Committee held hearings on electric vehicles.

The possibility of a major government research effort directed at replacing gasoline-powered vehicles represented a direct threat to both the automobile and the oil industries. They, and their ally within the Executive Branch, the Department of the Interior, argued vigorously against such a research effort. The electric industry and its ally, the Federal Power Commission, argued with equal vigor in favor of the possibilities of electric vehicles. The White House, anxious to avoid both a major political controversy and an expensive research undertaking in a tight budget year, headed off the congressional proposals by setting up a study by outside experts under the aegis of the Commerce Department. The oil and auto industries were well represented on the panel of outside experts. The panel recommended against any Federal support for research on electric or other nonpolluting vehicles,[2] but the pressure for such support has not abated and the controversy will undoubtedly reappear in the near future.

Research on the effects of pollution provides a necessary scientific basis for the setting of pollution control standards. But research by itself will not produce standards. This becomes evident as we examine the process of standard-setting.

STANDARD-SETTING

The establishment of standards is a crucial step in any pollution control program. Standards not only state the goals of the program, they also provide a measuring stick to determine the program's progress and a basis for determining what actions should be taken by the program. In a very real sense, standards are the "marching orders" for a pollution control agency. Together with compliance, they are the core of the pollution control process.

To understand the standard-setting process it is necessary to distinguish between three kinds of standards, all of which are necessary for pollution control. First, there are the community *goals,* which state the objectives of the program in qualitative, nonnumerical terms. "Water suitable for swimming" or "Air which will not produce disease in healthy members of the population" are examples of goals. Second, there are *water quality or ambient air standards.* These translate the goals into specific numerical levels of quality to be applied to a body of water or to the air circulating in a community. Thus, "No more than X parts of suspended solids in River Y," or "No more than X parts per million of sulfur dioxide for any 8-hour period in city Y," are water quality or ambient air standards. The term "criteria" is used in water pollution as the equivalent of water quality standards. In air pollution, criteria are not standards but descriptions of the effects of different levels of pollutants; that is, they are descriptive, not prescriptive. The third kind of standards are *emission or effluent standards.* Emission standards prescribe how much of what kind of pollution is to be allowed from any given source, for example, "No industrial plant can discharge effluent containing more than X parts of suspended solids into River Y," or "No power plant can use fuel containing more than X per cent of sulfur in city Y."

The establishment of goals is basically a political question, as we pointed out in Chapter 1. The balance which must be struck in the political arena has been well described by the Federal body responsible for setting radiation protection standards. "The use of radiation results in numerous benefits to man in medicine, industry, commerce, and research," states the Federal Radiation Council. "If those beneficial uses were fully exploited without regard to radiation protection, the resulting biological risk might well be considered too great. Reducing the risk to zero would virtually eliminate any radiation use, and result in the loss of all possible benefits. It is therefore necessary to strike some balance between maximum use and zero risk. In establishing radiation protection standards, the balancing of risk and benefit is a decision involving medical, social, economic, political, and other factors. Such a balance cannot be made on the basis of a precise mathematical formula but must be a matter of informed judgment."[3]

A community's designation of goals implies some kind of cost-benefit calculation, even though the calculation in most cases is intuitive or even unconscious. A community which decides that it wants to eliminate pollution in a given river to the extent that people can swim there is implicitly deciding that the benefits of being able to swim in the river are greater than the costs of eliminating the pollution. However, techniques are not now available, and probably never will be, to reduce the cost-benefit calculation to any kind of mathematical precision. The value which one community attaches to being able to swim may very well be different from that placed on swimming by the next community.

If there were complete knowledge of the effects of all pollutants, the transition from goals to quality standards would be almost automatic. Once it had been determined that River Y should be suitable for swimming, the scientists would be able to provide a listing of what level of control for each kind of pollutant was necessary to permit safe swimming. However, as we indicated above, such knowledge of effects is far from complete. In air pollution it is so incomplete that the distinction between goals and quality standards tends to become lost, and controversy often rages over numerical quality standards without any consideration of what the quality standards represent in terms of substantive goals. Without knowledge of the effects of particular pollutants, communities do not know what they are "buying" for the costs of establishing particular quality standards.

In some cases quality standards have been like Latin American constitutions, an expression of aspirations rather than intent; but most localities and states which have established quality standards have done so with the intention of carrying out enforcement. Before any enforcement can take place the community must also establish emission standards. Cease-and-desist orders cannot be issued to a river and enforcement conferences cannot be held with the ambient air in a city. Enforcement must be directed against polluters, not against pollution, and it is only emission standards which prescribe the action to be taken by polluters.

The development of emission standards, despite the fact that they represent the "teeth" in any control program, has generally been considered the domain of the technicians. Community controversy usually takes place over goals and quality standards but only rarely over emission standards. It is presumed that once the quality standards have been established the emission standards can be mathematically calculated, although in fact the transition from quality to emission standards involves a number of assumptions which are by no means mathematical or automatic.

In many cases emission standards are not directly tied to quality standards, but rather are based on some standard of "good practice." Thus, a community may simply determine that all industries within its jurisdiction shall install the best control devices currently available. The guidelines issued by the Department of the Interior for water quality standards state that municipalities are expected to provide secondary treatment for wastes. These kinds of emission standards are arbitrary in that they are not related to the achievement of goals or quality standards. The application of secondary treatment to all municipal wastes flowing into a particular river may make the river cleaner than it has to be or may leave it in a condition completely inadequate for the desired use, depending on the proportion of pollution contributed by municipalities, the size of the municipalities along the river, the amount of water flowing in the river, and a number of other factors.

In cases where emission standards are based on quality standards, the process of deriving the former from the latter is usually complex. The basic step is generally to calculate the percentage reduction necessary to get from existing levels to the quality standards and then to apply this same percentage reduction to existing emissions. To take an actual example, HEW's recommended sulfur standard for New York City was derived as follows: The desirable level of quality for ambient air was set at an annual mean concentration of sulfur dioxide no greater than 0.02 parts per million. This was the lowest level associated with increased respiratory disease death rates in man, with significant corrosion of metals, and with injury to perennial vegetation. It was determined that in New York the existing concentration of sulfur dioxide in the air needed to be reduced by 83 per cent to achieve the desired level. The total amount of sulfur dioxide emitted annually into the New York atmosphere (1,600,000 tons) was then divided by the total heat content of all coal and oil burned annually in the city (1,600 trillion British thermal units [BTU]), resulting in the figure of 2 pounds of sulfur dioxide per 1 million BTU. If an 83 per cent reduction was to be achieved, then only 17 per cent of the existing emissions could be allowed to continue. Seventeen per cent of 2 pounds of sulfur dioxide per 1 million BTU is 0.34 pounds of sulfur dioxide per 1 million BTU which, with slight rounding, was the emission standard announced for the New York area.[4]

The kind of straightforward approach to calculating emission standards which calls simply for an equal percentage reduction from all pollution sources involves a number of assumptions which are open to question. It ignores the question of costs, although in many cases it would probably be much less expensive to have certain polluters reduce their emissions by 95 per cent and others reduce their emissions by only 75 per cent, rather than both sources reducing emissions by 85 per cent. A simulation study by HEW revealed that for certain types of air pollution control objectives, the uniform reduction approach may cost seven times as much as an approach which utilizes variations in emission standards.[5] Thus the across-the-board standard may be the most equitable or the simplest to administer, but it is often not the least-cost solution.

The uniform reduction approach also does not take into account the location of the emission sources, meteorological conditions (in the case of air pollution), and other factors which influence the dispersion of the pollution. It does not consider changes in the amount of pollution which will occur in future years because of industrial expansion, plant relocation, or other factors. Alternatives to emission reduction, such as stream re-aeration in the case of water pollution or relocation of power plants in the case of air pollution, are usually not taken into account. In short, a number of simplifying assumptions are made, and if any of these assumptions were changed a different standard would probably result.

With the passage of the 1965 Water Quality Act and the 1967 Air Quality Act, standard-setting, has been put on a similar basis for air and water pollution. However, there remain a number of significant differences in the two areas and an examination of each will help to clarify further the standard-setting process.

AIR POLLUTION STANDARDS

The Air Quality Act lays down a series of steps to be followed in the establishment of air pollution control standards in given areas. These steps are *not* limited to areas of interstate air pollution, although enforcement action by the Federal government is limited to interstate air pollution except when Federal action is requested by the Governor of the state involved.

HEW begins the standard-setting process by designating "air quality control regions" containing communities in one or more states and by publishing "air quality criteria" and data on control techniques for particular pollutants. Each state included in an air quality control region then has 90 days to file a letter of intent stating that it will set appropriate standards and controls for the pollutant covered by the criteria. After filing the letter, the states have 180 days to adopt such standards applicable to each control region and 360 days to adopt a plan on how to achieve compliance with the standards. The standards become effective when approved by the Secretary of HEW, and if a state fails to adopt standards or its standards are not approved by HEW, then the department can promulgate its own standards for the region. If HEW promulgates the standards, the state is given an additional six months to adopt standards satisfactory to HEW, and if it fails to do so, the HEW standards become effective for the region. States may appeal standards set by HEW to a hearing board.[6]

As of this date, HEW has published criteria for sulfur oxides and particulate matter and has designated twenty metropolitan areas as air quality control regions.[7] Thirty-two areas are expected to be designated by the end of 1969, and an additional twenty-five areas by the summer of 1970. However, sufficient time has not yet elapsed for any state standards to have been approved.

A major key to the Air Quality Act standard-setting process is the "air quality criteria." HEW's publication of the criteria for some particular pollutant, such as sulfur oxides or particulate matter, triggers the standard-setting process. With the promulgation of the criteria and the recommended control techniques, the clock giving the states a certain amount of time to set standards for that particular pollutant begins to run. Furthermore, the act says that the state standards must be "consistent with the air quality criteria."[8] Thus in addition to starting the process, the criteria may well determine the outcome of the process. Many experts who have commented on the act have interpreted "consistent with" to mean "the same as."

HEW was first called on to publish criteria by the 1963 Clean Air Act. Under this act the criteria had no binding force but were designed simply to assist state and local governments in setting their own standards. But the act's description of criteria contained a basic ambiguity which was to be the source of considerable controversy. One section stated that "the Secretary shall compile and publish criteria reflecting accurately the latest scientific knowledge useful in indicating the kind and extent of such effects which may be expected from the presence of such air pollution agent (or combination of agents) in the air in varying quantities."[9] The next section read, "The Secretary may recommend to such air pollution control agencies . . . such criteria of air quality as in his judgment may be necessary to protect the public health and welfare."[10] Here were two quite different conceptions of what the criteria should be.

TABLE 7-1.
Proposed Air Quality Control Regions
(listed in the order in which designation is expected
to take place)

1. Washington, D.C.*	17. Hartford*
2. New York*	18. Indianapolis*
3. Chicago*	19. Minneapolis–St. Paul*
4. Philadelphia*	20. Milwaukee*
5. Denver*	21. Providence
6. Los Angeles*	22. Seattle-Tacoma*
7. St. Louis*	23. Louisville
8. Boston*	24. Dayton
9. Cincinnati*	25. Phoenix
10. San Francisco*	26. Houston
11. Cleveland*	27. Dallas–Ft. Worth
12. Pittsburgh*	28. San Antonio
13. Buffalo*	29. Birmingham
14. Kansas City*	30. Toledo
15. Detroit	31. Steubenville
16. Baltimore*	32. Chattanooga

Source: Dr. John Middleton, Director of NAPCA, in interview, *Mining Congress Journal* (October 1968), and NAPCA press releases.

*Already approved (as of October 25, 1969).

The first definition implied that the document should be a *descriptive* compilation of scientific findings. The second that the criteria were to be a standard, a *prescriptive* recommendation as to what the proper level of air quality should be. The confusion between descriptive criteria and prescriptive standards was repeated in the 1965 Water Quality Act, which stated that if the Secretary "determines that . . . State criteria and plans are consistent with [the requirements of the act], such State criteria and plans shall thereafter be the water quality standards applicable to . . . interstate water."[11]

The blurring of the distinction between criteria and standards violates the basic logic of the standard-setting process. If the criteria are a descriptive compilation of scientific findings, then it is only by combining criteria with goals that one can arrive at standards. There is no purely scientific way to arrive at a standard, because science only describes, it does not tell us what should be done. Insofar as the criteria are scientific they cannot prescribe standards, and insofar as the criteria attempt to lay down standards they are "unscientific." The political advantages of wrapping the cloak of scientific objectivity around the standard-setting process are obvious, but it is an abuse of logic to do so.

It took NAPCA more than three years to write and publish its first criteria, those for sulfur oxides.[12] The major part of the criteria publication consisted of summaries of 347 studies which had been done on the effects of sulfur oxides on man, plants, animals, and materials. The document also established a "recommended level," or standard, for sulfur oxides of an annual average concentration of 0.015 ppm. The standard was derived from a goal that the health of sensitive or susceptible segments of the population should not be adversely affected,[13] but the derivation of the standard from the goal was not made explicit. The problems of such a derivation are made clear by the finding of the Muskie committee that "In selecting indices of health effects the most prudent biological assumption is that there is no level of atmospheric pollution below which there can be absolute certainty that harmful effects will not occur to at least a few individuals when sufficiently large numbers of people are exposed."[14]

A storm of criticism followed the publication of the criteria for sulfur oxides. HEW was criticized for treating all the studies as if they were of equal scientific validity whereas it was obvious that they were not. The summaries of the studies were said to draw conclusions which the studies themselves did not. The recommended level was based on only two or three studies and the conclusions of those two or three were open to question. Although there had been some consultation with nongovernment scientists, no outside panel of experts had been organized to review the HEW work, a step which is customary in such cases. The diagrams and the summaries mingled long-term and short-term exposures as if they were the same, whereas the bodily mechanisms involved are quite different.

The standard recommended by the criteria for sulfur oxides was an extremely stringent one, and it threatened to reduce sharply the use of coal in any area where it was adopted. The coal industry was thus extremely vociferous in its criticisms of the criteria, and it succeeded in having the Senate Public Works Committee add to the 1967 Air Quality Act a provision that the criteria should be "re-evaluated" and if necessary "modified and reissued."[15] The 1967 act did not, however, remove the basic ambiguity concerning the nature of the criteria. Although the director of NAPCA testified to the Muskie committee at length about the distinction between criteria and standards, describing criteria as "an expression of scientific knowledge" and "descriptive,"[16] the new act stated that "The Secretary shall . . . issue . . . such criteria of air quality as in his judgment may be requisite for the protection of the public health and welfare."[17] To give operational meaning to "public health and welfare" could not be done scientifically any more in 1967 than in 1963.

On January 31, 1969, HEW issued a new version of the sulfur criteria. During the fourteen months between passage of the 1967 act and issuance of the new criteria, intense debate took place within HEW on how much the original document should be modified and particularly on whether the new version should recommend a minimum standard. The issue was resolved in a somewhat muddled but dramatic fashion.

Under the 1967 act, HEW was required to establish and consult with an advisory committee while formulating the criteria. In the fall of 1968 a majority of the members of the advisory committee complained that they were not being consulted in a manner consistent with the law. As a result, HEW held a final review meeting of the committee a few weeks before issuing the new criteria. At the review meeting the committee members understood that NAPCA had decided not to recommend a minimum standard.

After the meeting of the advisory committee, the NAPCA decision was reversed by C. C. Johnson, administrator of the Consumer Protection and Environmental Health Service, of which NAPCA was a part. Johnson insisted that the criteria should name a minimum desirable level, and the document which was sent to state officials at the end of January concluded with the statement that "on the basis of the foregoing information and data, it is reasonable and prudent to conclude that sulfur oxides of 300 ug/m3 (0.1 ppm) or more in the atmosphere over a period of 24 hours may produce adverse health effects in particular segments of the population."[18]

There was an immediate outcry against the naming of a specific figure. The National Coal Policy Conference's Newsletter headlined: "HEW Issues Criteria on Sulfur Oxides and Particulate Matter Which in Effect Establishes [sic] National Standards; Intent of Congress Violated." [19] The adverse reaction was sufficient to make HEW issue a new version of the criteria modifying the wording of the conclusion, but retaining the specific figure. [20]

Whether HEW will reject any proposed state standards which are more lenient than the number suggested in the new criteria remains to be seen. It may well be that more lenient standards will not be submitted, because almost no state has the expert personnel necessary to devise and defend a standard other than that recommended by HEW. The reliance of state and local control agencies on the Federal government for suggested standards is almost total. As one local official put it to the Senate Subcommittee on Air and Water Pollution, "Since the Federal Government has been very helpful with technical assistance in the past, with their experience, we have complete faith in any kind of standards that they would send to us. . . . So, we are waiting for the Federal Government to send us some set of standards that we will strive to reach." [21]

Not all local officials are quite as pliant as the one quoted above, but the lack of experience and preparation of most states and many localities for setting standards indicates that the Federal influence will be dominant. Industry groups which are adversely affected by the proposed standards can be expected to lobby vigorously at the state level for more lenient state standards. Some of these industries, notably the coal and oil people, can provide some expertise to the states, thereby slightly counterbalancing the influence of HEW. But given the overwhelming knowledge and experience at the Federal level, the political sensitivity of dealing with public health, and the fact that HEW holds the trump card of final approval or disapproval, it is unlikely that many states will choose to fight the Federal criteria.

Having granted the dominant influence of the Federal government in setting air pollution standards, it is worth exploring the process by which such standards are arrived at. The HEW proposed standard for sulfur oxides is not only the first but also the most politically sensitive standard to be established. An account of the process by which it was promulgated provides insight into the setting of standards generally as well as into some of the political factors at work in air pollution control.

THE CASE OF THE SULFUR OXIDES STANDARD

Air pollution officials in the Public Health Service had concluded soon after the Donora incident that sulfur oxides were the major health threat among the numerous different air pollutants. When the 1963 Clean Air Act called for HEW to issue criteria for various pollutants, it was decided that the criteria for sulfur oxides should take top priority. However, work proceeded slowly because of the shortage of medical and biological personnel necessary to compile such a document.

In 1965, HEW was forced to reach a conclusion on a desirable level of sulfur oxides control because of a decision to issue an Executive Order dealing with the control of pollution from Federal installations. The formulation of the order was the responsibility of the Bureau of the Budget, a part of the Executive Office of the President, but the technical information and the recommended standards would have to come from HEW.[22]

HEW, with work on its criteria having just begun, settled on a proposed limit for Federal installations of not more than 0.7 per cent sulfur for coal and not more than 0.9 per cent sulfur for oil. This standard was based on the few studies which had been done and on the judgment of the chief of HEW's Air Pollution Division. Aware of the political implications of the sulfur issue, the Budget Bureau requested the coal and oil industry to comment on the proposed sulfur limitations. Reaction by industry representatives was rapid and adverse.

In April 1965, representatives of the Budget Bureau, HEW, and the coal and oil industry met. No decisions were recorded, but HEW made it clear that they believed that the 0.7 per cent and 0.9 per cent standards were the only reasonable ones, at least for Federal facilities in the largest metropolitan areas, and the industry representatives made it clear that they thought no sulfur standard was needed. The coal and oil people were less worried about the impact of the proposed restrictions on Federal fuel purchasing than about the Federal standard being adopted by state and local control agencies throughout the nation. They reasoned, probably correctly, that control officials would operate on the assumption that what was a proper standard for Federal facilities was a proper standard for all local areas with serious pollution problems.

The industry representatives, seeing no signs of compromise from HEW or the Budget Bureau, turned to Congress for assistance. In July, Rep. Oren Harris, chairman of the House Committee on Interstate and Foreign Commerce which had jurisdiction over all health and pollution legislation, informed Wilbur Cohen, the Undersecretary of HEW, that he wanted assurance that regulations for air pollution from Federal facilities would not be issued, at least during the current session of Congress. HEW and the Budget Bureau, not wishing to jeopardize the 1965 amendments to the Clean Air Act and the numerous health bills which were pending in Harris's committee, decided that they had to comply. Accordingly, Cohen wrote to Harris, telling him, "The Director of the Budget Bureau and I have considered this matter and we agree that sulfur dioxide standards for Federal installations should not be promulgated at this time, but that further consideration and study will be necessary." [23]

During the fall HEW and the Budget Bureau worked together in redrafting the proposed Executive Order. HEW, its work on the criteria having progressed and some new research findings having been made, decided to make the proposed sulfur standards considerably more stringent. The department decided that the limit should be 0.2 per cent sulfur for coal and 0.3 per cent sulfur for oil. However, HEW suggested these limits might be applied only for facilities in New York, Chicago, and Philadelphia.

With the new draft in hand, the Budget Bureau, in January 1966, initiated a new round of negotiations with the coal and oil representatives. A series of meetings was held, and, unlike the 1965 confrontation, serious bargaining took place between the industry and Budget Bureau representatives. HEW was present at the meetings but did not take much part in the negotiations, insisting that its standards were the only possible ones.

In March, Irving Lewis, chief of the Budget Bureau's Health and Welfare Division, drew up a compromise which met with the approval of all the parties. It called for HEW to issue sulfur regulations for Federal facilities in New York, Chicago, and Philadelphia within six months after the issuance of the Executive Order. Federal facilities in other communities would be required to burn "the lowest sulfur content fuel that is reasonably available." Reasonable availability was to be determined by each individual Federal agency, but the determination was to consider, among other factors, "price, firmness of supply, extent of existing pollution, and assurance of supply under adverse weather and natural disaster conditions." Thus the compromise delayed the crucial decision for six months but left it firmly in the hands of HEW. On May 26, 1966, the Executive Order was issued.[24]

In the months following the promulgation of the Executive Order, the issue over Federal facilities was joined with two other decisions, both of which bore directly on sulfur standards. The first was the pending publication of the criteria for sulfur oxides. The second was the HEW abatement conference dealing with air pollution in the New York–New Jersey metropolitan area. The conference, in January 1967, had recommended to the Secretary of HEW a limitation of 0.2 per cent sulfur in coal and 0.3 per cent sulfur in oil for space heating and a limitation of 1 per cent sulfur coal and oil in power generation plants. The Secretary, however, had taken no immediate action on the recommendation.

It was clear that HEW would have to be consistent in recommending a sulfur standard in all three cases—Federal facilities, the criteria, and the New York abatement conference. As the implications of the decision on sulfur became apparent, reverberations were felt in various parts of the Federal bureaucracy. The State Department began receiving cablegrams from the Venezuelan Embassy indicating the extreme concern of the Venezuelan government about the effect of the proposed standards on oil imports. Venezuela is one of America's staunchest allies in South America, income from oil imports constitutes more than half of the Venezuelan government's revenue, and most of the Venezuelan oil is high-sulfur. The State Department was also concerned about the diversion of low-sulfur coal to domestic consumption, since much of the low-sulfur coal mined in the United States was being exported to Europe and was thus an important factor in maintaining a favorable balance of payments. The Department of the Interior and the Office of Emergency Planning began considering changes in oil import quotas to relieve the plight of the Venezuelans and to supply sufficient low-sulfur fuel to meet domestic needs. The Federal Power Commission, guardian of the country's natural gas supply, expressed concern over the possibility of greatly increased demands for natural gas, a fuel which contained almost no sulfur. The Commission was also worried about the impact of the sulfur regulations on its primary constituency, the electric power producers.

On November 22, 1966, HEW issued the proposed regulations for Federal facilities in the three cities. The regulations were based on the ambient air standard of 0.015 ppm annual average which was to be recommended in the criteria. This translated into limitations of 0.2 per cent sulfur coal and 0.3 per cent sulfur oil in New York City and 0.4 per cent sulfur coal and 0.6 per cent sulfur oil in Chicago and Philadelphia. The compliance date for facilities was October 1, 1968.

HEW allowed thirty days for comment on the Federal facility regulations, and this was extended to sixty days at the request of the coal industry. The reaction of the coal industry was predictable. "Let us consider," said the comments submitted jointly by the National Coal Policy Conference, the National Coal Association, and the United Mine Workers,

certain predictable impacts if the restrictions lead to their logical consequence. If coal were barred from all metropolitan areas— which would be the logical ultimate effect of the proposed regulation: A market for 129.5 million tons of coal in the electric utility market alone would be wiped out. . . . This would in turn affect jobs, both directly and indirectly, for more than 50,000 families. This means an estimated $360 million in annual wages, at current levels, for the men engaged directly in the production and transportation of coal would be affected. Some $200 million in the purchase of services and supplies would be lost to the economy . . . take away coal and there will be released a chain reaction of economic consequences the full measure of which would be staggering.[25]

There was no question that the sulfur regulations represented a decision which had major ramifications for the nation's economy. America's economy is based on the consumption of fuel, and the regulations were a possible prelude to a major shift in the nation's pattern of fuel use. But there was also little question that the Federal government was not organized to consider such ramifications. HEW based its regulations almost exclusively on considerations of health and did not consider economics to be within its sphere of concern. During the time when the regulations were being considered, the National Center for Air Pollution Control had on its staff only one practicing economist, and he was on loan to another agency for much of the period. No agency of the government had responsibility for considering the overall pattern of fuel usage,[26] and contacts between HEW and the agencies responsible for some part of the fuel picture were sporadic or nonexistent.

On March 21, 1967, the Secretary of HEW approved the recommendations of the New York abatement conference. The regulations for Federal facilities were given final approval by HEW the following day. No change was made in the Federal facility regulations despite the adverse comments from industry sources and the foreboding of some Federal officials that greater political storms were to follow. The coal industry shifted its emphasis to obtaining more research funds for desulfurization of stack gas, a technique which held the potential of permitting high-sulfur coal to be used in areas with stringent pollution regulations because the sulfur would be removed in the smokestack after the fuel was burned. The industry also directed its lobbying efforts in Congress toward getting favorable language into the 1967 Air Quality Act.

The concerns of the State Department, the Federal Power Commission, and other agencies affected by the regulations had not abated. Sentiment began to crystallize in favor of a State Department proposal for an interagency committee on air pollution, which would at least provide access by the other agencies to the HEW decision-making process. But any potential dilution of HEW's authority over air pollution was complicated by rumors and by threats from the coal and oil people to transfer authority over air pollution from HEW to the Interior Department. Animosity between the two agencies reached new heights, and any change in the status of HEW's jurisdiction would have been viewed in the light of the struggle between the two departments.

The Budget Bureau decided that pressures within the Executive Branch generated by the sulfur regulations were reaching an intolerable level. The Bureau thus drafted a presidential letter to a dozen Federal agencies which (1) reaffirmed the jurisdiction of HEW over air pollution; (2) called for a major increase in funds for research on desulfurization and designated the Office of Science and Technology as a "referee" to allocate the research efforts between HEW and Interior; and (3) called for a study by HEW and the Council of Economic Advisers of the "effects of air pollution control on industry and trade, both foreign and domestic." The letter, which was signed by the President on April 21, 1967, succeeded in easing bureaucratic tensions, at least for the moment.[27]

The controversy surrounding sulfur regulations continues, and undoubtedly will continue for a number of years. Adjustments in the nation's fuel economy have already taken place. Interior has proposed a major liberalization in its oil import quotas to make available more low-sulfur-content fuel oil, and there has been a dramatic increase in the construction of nuclear plants for power generation. Both of these changes have been bitterly fought by the coal industry in the halls of Congress and at the state and local level. However, it should also be noted that coal production has risen steadily since 1960 and showed no signs of being reduced in 1968 òr 1969.[28]

The case of sulfur regulations illustrates the complex interplay of different forces in the making of a major government decision. Foreign policy, the nation's economy, and public health all had to be considered. The pressure of private interest groups, interbureaucratic rivalries, congressional influence, and the relations among Federal, state, and local governments all weighed heavily in the decisions. The process of making the decisions was in many respects haphazard and irrational, but the outcome gives no support to a theory of industrial control over decisions which have a major impact on the economy. The sulfur case also shows the crucial role played by scientists in the making of pollution policy. The scientists set the parameters for the decision on standards by estimating the effects of given levels of pollutants. They went even further, however, and advocated specific standards based on their view of the public interest being the goal of eliminating all detectable health effects. Their advocacy was probably a constructive force, but they were clearly acting as political decisionmakers, not as scientists.

WATER POLLUTION STANDARDS

The 1965 Water Quality Act required the states to designate the use to which each stretch of water would be put (fishing, drinking, swimming, etc.) and then establish quantitative standards appropriate for such uses. The states were also required to submit a plan describing how the standards were to be implemented.

The Secretary of the Interior has approved the standards of all fifty states, although in a number of cases nominal Federal approval has been given with extensive exceptions that remain to be negotiated. The task of reviewing the standards at the Federal level has been formidable because, in contrast to the provisions of the Air Quality Act, all states were required to set standards for all interstate waters. Many of the submissions ran to 1,000 pages or more.

The process of settling water pollution standards under the 1965 act has been characterized by cooperation and negotiation between the Federal and state levels. Interior worked closely with a number of states in developing the standards. Not only did the department issue a set of "Guidelines" to the states for developing the standards but, as the Assistant Secretary for Water Pollution Control put it, "In many states we moved in and gave them some direction as to how to get the job done." [29] The approval process has been characterized by bargaining over the standards, and even when Interior has reached the limits of bargaining it has not rejected the state proposals outright. Secretary of the Interior Udall told the Muskie committee, "We are not going to say to the Governors of the States concerned, 'Your standards are not adequate and therefore the Federal Government is moving in to set the standards.' We don't want to be arbitrary; we want to give the States every opportunity to come up to the level that we feel is adequate. Instead, we will send the standards back to these States for revision."[30]

The attitude of cooperation and negotiation is due partially to a tradition of cooperation, partially to the political realities of a decentralized system. The latter is well illustrated by the fact that in the case of at least one state its congressional delegation reviewed and approved the proposed water quality standards before they were submitted to Interior.[31] Cooperation is also made necessary by the nature of the tasks to be performed. Each level is dependent on the other to get the job done. The states rely on the Federal government for research, for technical assistance, and for money. They are also well aware that final authority in many cases, such as the standard-setting process, rests at the Federal level. The Federal government is dependent on the states not only for the political support necessary to clean up the rivers but also for technical and administrative support. The commissioner of FWPCA told Muskie, "I appeared before you in opposition to the concept of mandatory Federal standards, and my basic objection was that I saw it as an administrative monstrosity . . . I don't think the agency that I head or any other agency of the Federal Government could have gone about the job of setting the water quality standards in less than 5 to 6 to 10 years."[32]

Despite the close contact between state and Federal levels, however, the process of setting the standards has not taken place without controversy. One state, Iowa, has resisted the Federal government almost every step of the way. After more than three years of increasingly abrasive negotiations, the Secretary of the Interior finally decided that compromise with the state was impossible, and he moved to establish Federal standards for Iowa's discharges into the Mississippi and Missouri

Rivers and twenty-five smaller interstate streams. In April 1969, two formal conferences were held with Iowa officials, and in October Secretary Hickel ordered the proposed Federal standards published in the *Federal Register*. Whether Iowa will now accept the Federal standards remains to be seen.

The most widespread and important dispute over standards has concerned the so-called "anti-degradation" provision. Within six weeks after the submission deadline, Interior had approved water quality standards for ten states. Although some of the standards had been developed in close cooperation with Federal officials and had been submitted before the actual deadline, the review given to the standards by the department was hasty.[33] As the content of the approved standards became public knowledge, Interior began to draw the ire of the conservation groups.

The National Wildlife Federation was the most vehement in its objections. The president of the Federation wrote to Secretary Udall in the fall of 1967 stating that he was shocked that "FWPCA officials felt that authority in classification by use of interstate waters was the sole prerogative of the states," and "that 'pure water' can be downgraded and polluted legally under the terms of the Federal act, as long as it meets standards accepted by Interior for the specific use designated by the State."[34]

During the fall and winter the criticism voiced by the conservationists was seconded by influential members of Congress, including Senator Muskie. Attention focused primarily on the issue of whether unpolluted water could be allowed to receive some pollutants, providing the degree of pollution did not fall below the water quality standards established for the highest use of the water. The issue split the ranks of Interior, with the Assistant Secretary for Water Pollution Control supporting the conservationists and the commissioner of FWPCA opposing them.

Secretary Udall was faced with a difficult decision. If he approved a policy which did not permit any effluents into unpolluted water, he risked the strong opposition of the state-elected officials and the industries whose cooperation was necessary if the standards system was to succeed. There was a danger that the whole intergovernmental balance in the standard-setting process would be upset, because such an anti-degradation provision would at least potentially give the Federal government veto power over all new industrial development located along such "pure" waters. There was also the danger that economic development in some states would be seriously handicapped, and there was the embarrassment of admitting that the department had erred in approving some of the water quality standards. On the other hand, if Udall did not issue an anti-degradation policy he risked losing the support of the conservation groups and the congressmen who held the key to the future of the water pollution control program. He also would put himself in the position of favoring industrial development over "clean water," a posture which might do irreparable harm to the department's future pollution control efforts.

On February 8, 1968, Udall announced that henceforth all state standards would have to contain an anti-degradation provision and that states whose standards had already been approved although they did not include such a provision would be asked to revise them to conform with the new policy. The basic content of the provision was outlined as follows:

> Waters whose existing quality is better than the established standards as of the date on which such standards become effective will be maintained at their existing high quality. These and other waters of the State will not be lowered in quality unless and until it has been affirmatively demonstrated to the State water pollution control agency and the Department of the Interior that such change is justifiable as a result of necessary economic or social development and will not interfere with or become injurious to any assigned uses made of, or presently possible in, such waters.[35]

Udall's decision did not put an end to the controversy, but rather kindled the fires of opposition. Criticism came from the Western Governors' Conference, the Southern Governors' Conference, the Association of Attorneys' General, and the U.S. Chamber of Commerce. Governor John Love of Colorado declared, "As we Western Governors have long realized, and as I believe Eastern Governors are more and more coming to realize, the control of the use and development of water is tantamount to absolute control of the state. For we Governors to accept such an edict and to grant such power to any agency would be no less than traitorous."[36]

Udall met the opposition head-on. "There are some who are rising up to oppose this policy," he told the Advertising Council. "This is unfortunate. If the opposition gathers enough momentum, it could set the big water clean-up back 20 years."[37] But attempts were also made to reassure the opponents of the new policy. The new Assistant Secretary for Water Pollution Control told state officials that the anti-degradation provision was only a stop-gap measure. "We are talking about those high quality interstate waters," he said, "in which fish and other aquatic life propagation now flourishes and is a beneficial use as designated in the water quality standards of a State, but for which we do not now have sufficient data to determine beyond doubt that the criteria adopted in the standards is [sic] equal at least to the existing high quality . . . all we are asking, therefore, is a commitment by the States to preserve their high quality waters as best they can until the knowledge gap is overcome and the regular procedures and requirements on changing and revising standards can be followed as they are spelled out in the Act."[38]

It is uncertain at this point whether the anti-degradation issue has been laid to rest. As of April 1969, the water quality standards of nineteen states contained an anti-degradation provision. Thus more than thirty states have not accepted the FWPCA policy and opponents of the provision have discussed seeking Federal legislation to rescind the Udall decision. The entire controversy illustrates the delicate balance of Federal-state relations and the politically explosive nature of the standard-setting process.

Other problems in connection with the 1965 act have been considerably less troublesome than the anti-degradation issue but have nevertheless posed significant issues for the policy-makers. One of these difficulties has been the unofficial requirement that all wastes receive secondary treatment. Interior's guidelines for setting water quality standards state that "no standard will be approved which does not require all wastes, prior to discharge into any interstate water, to receive the best practicable treatment or control unless it can be demonstrated that a lesser degree of treatment or control will provide for water quality enhancement commensurate with proposed present and future water uses."[39] This would seem to require secondary treatment of almost all wastes, but such a requirement has met with significant opposition from industry and from state officials who find it arbitrary and inconsistent with the principle of setting standards according to use. It is in fact inconsistent with the use principle, and this has led to some rather tortured explanations by Interior officials. The Assistant Secretary for Water Pollution Control told the NAM: "We have been accused of insisting upon Federal standards which require industry to adopt secondary treatment or its equivalent . . . I confess that in our discussions with the States we have urged a general upgrading of treatment to the equivalent of secondary simply in order to achieve the level of stream quality desired. We have not demanded universal secondary treatment but simply that degree of treatment or control which will provide water quality enhancement commensurate with proposed present and future water uses. Of course, in many instances that degree of treatment is the equivalent of secondary, and in most instances the States themselves have required it in their standards."[40]

Another difficulty has been the total omission of interstate agencies from the standard-setting provisions of the act. Although the Department of the Interior informally gave its support to the standards developed by the Delaware River Basin Commission, other interstate bodies have played almost no role in the standard-setting process. In approving the state standards, Interior has tried to ensure compatibility between adjacent states with jurisdiction over parts of the same river; but it has not considered river basins as single units as it tries to do in its planning efforts. The commissioner of FWPCA stated, ". . . practically, if we were to try to negotiate out an organized concept on the Potomac, on the Columbia, on the Ohio, on the Mississippi . . . I think it would be July of 1973, and we still would not have approved many standards."[41] The locus of political power in the state capitals and the provisions of the act have made the use of the logical unit of planning (river basins) unfeasible. The drafters of the Air Quality Act have taken steps to minimize this problem, but the act's emphasis on regional control will undoubtedly cause problems in reconciling the need for interstate coordination with the need for Federal cooperation with the individual states.

One final problem is worth mention, not only because it is important in itself but also because it indicates an underlying characteristic of the Federal air and water pollution control programs. FWPCA put primary emphasis on the development of the standards and said little to the states about the plans for implementation. In almost every state the implementation plan was developed, almost as an afterthought, in the last three to six weeks before the submission deadline.[42] Consequently, the plans were of almost uniformly poor quality and almost totally lacking in specifics. While the states must share the blame for this, it is clear that the minimized importance of the plans derived from the attitude of FWPCA. This attitude, in turn, derives from the dominance of scientists and technicians in the FWPCA hierarchy. For example, the initial task of reviewing the state standards was assigned to the regional offices, and every one of the nine FWPCA regional directors is an engineer. A scientist or engineer tends to be happier dealing with water quality standards than with the politics or economics of implementing those standards, and this professional bias accounts for much of the emphasis put on technical considerations in the formulation of the state submissions.

Secretary Udall has called the water quality standards program "the real beginning point,"[43] and the same statement could be made about the air quality standards program. The standard-setting process is the basic step which sets the pattern for future actions in controlling pollution. But the establishment of standards is a beginning, not an end. Once the standards become official, the long struggle to make them a reality must begin. This struggle is the compliance process. And the successful outcome of compliance must be the ultimate goal of any pollution control program.

CHAPTER 8

Compliance

COMPLIANCE is the process whereby existing pollution is halted or reduced or potential pollution is prevented. The prevailing legal framework for compliance in the United States is what might be called "enforcement," the establishment of effluent standards and the legal prosecution of those who violate the standards. However, within this legal framework there are many strategies which a governmental agency can pursue in order to achieve compliance, and most agencies rely on techniques such as persuasion, negotiation, and education far more than on formal legal sanctions.

The establishment of effluent standards and the legal prosecution of those who violate the standards is a "common-sense" approach which follows the model of all criminal law enforcement. As in criminal law enforcement, a high degree of voluntary compliance is necessary. However, controlling pollution presents problems which are quite different from those of controlling burglary or fraud. The enforcement of standards against individual polluters may be quite inefficient in terms of time, money, and results, and bargaining with violators may often be necessary. Especially in controlling water pollution, where there are a wide variety of alternatives which can be utilized, methods which treat the stream as a whole, such as stream re-aeration or low-flow augmentation, sometimes may be much less expensive and accomplished much more rapidly than trying to get each individual source of pollution to treat its own wastes.

The major alternative which has been proposed to the standards and prosecution approach is a system of economic penalties or effluent fees.[1] This involves the establishment of a schedule of fees for emitting given amounts of pollutants into a stream or into the air. Each polluter must then pay a certain amount to a control commission, according to how much of what kind of pollutant he has emitted. The schedule of fees can be adjusted upward or downward to reach any desired level of stream quality or ambient air, although in the ideal system the fees would be based on the amount of damages (or costs) caused by the pollution. The money collected from the fees is used to provide centralized pollution control facilities and also for monitoring and other activities of the control commission.

The effluent fee system has been promoted primarily by economists who see it as a way of achieving the optimal economic balance between the costs of pollution damage and the costs of pollution control.[2] The technical obstacles to determining such a balance, particularly the cost of obtaining the necessary data, are very great.[3] But the political obstacles may be even greater, because it is unlikely that economists and other technicians will be left free to set whatever fee schedules they consider desirable. Neither the local chapter of the Izaak Walton League nor the local pulp mill will feel bound by the economists' formulas, and the optimal economic balance will be adjusted by the political balance which prevails in the particular area.[4]

The major advantages of effluent fees are that they allow each polluter to control his pollution in the most economical way and that they encourage the establishment of the least-cost control system for a river basin or an airshed considered as a whole. In effect, the system utilizes the workings of the free market economy, controlling pollution by internalizing the so-called "externalities" of firms or municipalities by making them pay for their use of air or water. The administration of an effluent fee system might be simpler than the standards and prosecution approach, since, at least in theory, the activities of the control commission would consist only of setting the air or water quality standards, establishing the fee schedule, monitoring effluents, and billing the polluters. The initiative for installing control systems would rest with each polluter rather than with a centralized public body.

With all these advantages, why hasn't the effluent fee system been applied in the United States? At the present time it is probably not feasible to apply it to the control of air‧ pollution. The sources of air pollution are so numerous and reliable monitoring instruments so expensive that the key step of monitoring all individual effluents is not possible, given current technology. To apply the system to water pollution control it is necessary to have a control commission which encompasses an entire river basin and which has sufficient authority to impose fees. In the United States the Delaware River Basin Commission and the Tennessee Valley Authority are the only bodies which come close to having the requisite authority, and they do not currently have such authority. There is also the question of which river basin should go first in trying the system. Because of the experimental nature of the approach, neither the Federal government nor anyone else would encourage instituting the system in all river basins at once. And yet since the consequences of the system are not fully known, and the degree of compliance to pollution standards would hopefully be higher than it is at present, industries in any basin would oppose the system and officials in the affected states would be reluctant to pioneer it because of possible adverse effects on economic development. Thus, even if there were many river basin commissions equipped with the legal and political power to impose an effluent fee system, none of them would be eager to be the first to apply it.

Effluent fees have been criticized by some as constituting a "license to pollute." Insofar as the concept of effluent fees is based on collecting damages equal to the marginal costs of pollution, it would permit some pollution to occur, specifically that amount of pollution which is economically "optimal." However, given the impossibility of assigning accurate dollar values to many of the costs of pollution, such as the cost of ugliness or of foregone recreational opportunities, any effluent fee system would probably be based on standards derived from the same considerations as the currently used enforcement standards. Also, since current enforcement efforts can hardly be considered to have worked perfectly, the real question is not which system is theoretically perfect but which is actually capable of achieving the highest degree of compliance most efficiently.

An accurate assessment of the actual accomplishments of an effluent fee system necessarily entails a prediction of the politics of the system. Political factors are a potential weakness in the system, because it might be more difficult to muster public support for a control commission which was using effluent fees than for one which was employing the traditional standards and prosecution procedure. While the public might approve of the general idea of an effluent fee system, the actual setting of the fees is the kind of technical decision which it finds difficult to follow or understand. Industry groups, on the other hand, would understand the fees (since they would have to pay) and would follow such decisions closely. There is thus the risk that the public would be apathetic and would permit the fees to be set at too low a level to achieve the desired water quality. Effluent fees would not be imposed in a political vacuum, and the pressures exerted by industries and some public officials for lenient pollution controls would still be present.

Two examples lend some indirect empirical evidence to the fear of political forces undermining the effectiveness of an effluent fee system. In the Ruhr Valley in Germany a type of effluent fee system has been established, although on a scale and in a manner which makes the example not very applicable to the United States. The control bodies which set the fees, the "Genossenschaften," are heavily weighted in favor of the industrial polluters, and the outcomes of the system have included devoting one entire river to waste disposal. Regardless of the merits of this outcome, it is unlikely that it would have much political appeal here.[5] The other example is the setting of sewer rental charges, a practice common in many American communities. Such charges are in many respects analogous to effluent fees, and in most communities they have been set at a level considerably lower than that necessary to cover the costs of treating the sewage.[6]

One other major approach to achieving compliance is the use of economic incentives, such as tax credits for the installation of pollution control equipment. Economic incentives can serve only as a supplement to, and not as a substitute for, other major approaches. It has been proven by the sad experience of the localities which have instituted incentives but not penalties that industries require a stick as well as a carrot to make them take action. We have already discussed some of the disadvantages of providing tax credits, but economic incentives do encourage ,compliance by reducing the costs of such compliance to private industry.

FEDERAL ENFORCEMENT

The basic procedure for Federal enforcement against polluters is the same for air and water pollution. First a conference is held under the aegis of the Federal pollution control agency. The conference establishes a schedule for cleaning up the pollution which allows at least six months for action to be taken. If at the end of the six months sufficient progress has not been made, the Secretary may call a public hearing. There is a mandatory six-months delay after the public hearing and then, if compliance is still not satisfactory, the Secretary may request the Attorney General to bring suit against the polluters.

The initiation of enforcement action by the Federal government is generally limited to pollution which originates in one state but endangers the health or welfare of persons in another. The consent or request of the Governor of the state is necessary for a Federal action dealing with purely intrastate pollution. There are two significant exceptions to the interstate-intrastate differentiation. The Secretary of the Interior is authorized to initiate enforcement proceedings when "substantial economic injury results from the inability to market shellfish or shellfish products in interstate commerce because of pollution . . ."[7] This provision was enacted in 1965 to provide some relief for an industry which is particularly hard-hit by water pollution. The other exception is that the Secretary of HEW is authorized to seek immediate Federal court action in situations where pollution "is presenting an imminent and substantial endangerment to the health of persons" and state or local authorities have not acted to abate it.[8] This rather drastic procedure was placed in the 1967 act as a response to criticisms that in the case of a severe air pollution episode the lengthy procedures of the normal enforcement process would be useless and the Federal government would be forced to stand idly by while lives were lost.

The 1965 Water Quality Act authorized a greatly streamlined version of the enforcement procedure, permitting the Secretary of the Interior to eliminate both the conference and the public hearing in enforcing the standards established under the act. The Secretary must notify a violator of the standards 180 days before legal action is taken, but after such notice has been given and the required time has elapsed, the Secretary can ask the Justice Department to institute suit. Parallel provisions for enforcement of interstate air quality standards were included in the 1967 Air Quality Act.

The first actions under the new procedure were announced in September 1969, when the Secretary of the Interior gave formal notice to four steel companies and a mining company of violation of water quality standards.[9] Air quality standards under the 1967 act have not yet been established, and thus the new enforcement procedure has not been applied to air polluters. It is too soon to know what actual experience under the new enforcement procedures will be. The older conference-public hearing procedure has the advantage of being able to cover a large geographic area and a large number of polluters in a single action. An action under the new procedure, because it leads directly to court action, usually can only be applied to one pollution source at a time. Thus the older procedure may still be used in the future. For this reason, and because all of the existing Federal enforcement experience has been under the older procedure, it is worth examining the conference-public hearing process in more detail.

The conference stage of the enforcement procedure is legally a somewhat peculiar proceeding. Although it is the first step in a legally defined process leading eventually to court action, the conference itself is not run under court-type rules and it is not considered to be an adversary proceeding. The individual polluters are not parties to the conference, and in water pollution conferences they do not testify unless invited by the state control agencies. In 1967 the air pollution enforcement procedure was changed to require that all "interested parties" receive notice of the conference and an opportunity to present their views. The conference has been used as an informal meeting between the Federal control agency and its state and local counterparts for the purpose of mutually agreeing on a schedule of remedial measures, and also as a vehicle for publicizing the existence of pollution in a particular area.

The public hearing is a much more formal process. It takes place before a hearing board which consists of five or more persons appointed by the Secretary. Each of the states involved in the case can appoint one member of the board, and a majority of the members of the board must be persons who are not employees of the Federal department which initiated the enforcement action. The alleged polluters—whether an industry, individual, or governmental unit—are made direct participants in the hearing. Findings are made by the hearing board on the evidence presented, and it recommends to the Secretary the measures which must be taken to abate the pollution. The Secretary, if he approves the hearing board's findings and recommendations, sends them to the polluters and the state agencies along with a notice specifying a schedule for the accomplishment of the abatement measures.

Filing of a suit in Federal court, the final stage of the enforcement process, has occurred only twice. In water pollution only one case, a suit against the city of St. Joseph, Missouri, has been tried by the Federal courts. The conference involving pollution of the Missouri River by the city of St. Joseph was held in 1957 and was one of the first to be initiated by the Federal government. After the citizens of St. Joseph refused to approve a bond issue to provide the funds necessary for the construction of a treatment plant and connecting sewers, a public hearing was held in 1959. In 1960 the citizens again voted, the bond issue was defeated even more decisively, and the Federal government then filed suit in the Federal District Court. A court order, calling for completion of the necessary treatment facilities by 1963, was issued in 1961. In 1967 the city had completed work on the treatment plant but had only half completed installation of the sewers. The District Court has retained jurisdiction in the case, and in 1967 it ordered the city to expedite work on the projects. However, city officials contend that they cannot complete all the projects necessary to provide primary treatment for the city's waste until 1973.[10]

In air pollution one enforcement case has been heard by the courts but has not yet been finally decided. The first Federal abatement conference was held in 1965 to examine pollution reaching the state of Delaware from a rendering plant located in Bishop, Maryland. When the Bishop plant failed to take any remedial action a public hearing was held in 1967, and in 1968 the Secretary of HEW requested the Attorney General to bring suit. The Federal District Court in Baltimore heard the case on March 3 and 4, 1969, but the court adjourned the hearing because there were few documented instances of pollution from the plant reaching Delaware, and the court stated that it "would prefer to have more evidence in the case than we have now, before deciding the case . . ." HEW and the Delaware Air and Water Resources Commission are now gathering additional evidence to present to the court.[11]

Two aspects of air pollution enforcement differentiate it from Federal powers in controlling water pollution. First is the authority of HEW to control emissions from new motor vehicles. The department enforces its standards for new vehicles by testing a sample number of each vehicle having different motor-transmission combinations, as supplied by the manufacturers prior to the production runs. Test data are also required from the manufacturers. Compliance with the Federal standards must rest with the states once the vehicles go into use, but the authority of the Federal government to set and enforce standards for new motor vehicles is greater than for any other type of pollution. However, the Water Quality Improvement Act would give similar authority to the Federal government to control pollution from vessels.

The second differentiating feature of air pollution enforcement is the power of the Secretary of HEW to deal with potential sources of pollution, such as a proposal to construct a large power plant or paper mill. The Clean Air Act states: "If, in the judgment of the Secretary, an air pollution problem of substantial significance may result from discharge or discharges into the atmosphere, he may call a conference concerning this potential air pollution problem. . . ."[12] The results of the conference are advisory only, and the regular enforcement procedure cannot be used to prevent pollution before it occurs. Although this authority is not limited to interstate pollution, it has not been formally used by HEW. The major reasons for this are the limitations on the resources of NAPCA and the pressure to deal with existing pollution sources. Also, the authority over potential sources can only be applied to one or perhaps two sources of air pollution, whereas many sources of pollution can be covered in an abatement conference called under the regular enforcement process.

The control of air and water pollution from Federal facilities is carried out under the authority of the basic pollution legislation and of an Executive order issued by President Nixon in February 1970. The Nixon order superseded similar directives which had been issued by President Johnson.[13] The major obstacle in the control of pollution from Federal facilities is money. In 1967, the total amount of funds needed to control air and water pollution from Federal sources was estimated at several hundred million dollars. Since then more than $100 million has been appropriated to curb pollution from Federal facilities, but the appropriations have not been sufficient to meet the five-year timetable established in 1967.

The pollution caused by the recipients of Federal grants, contracts, and licenses has not received sufficient attention. The Senate Public Works Committee noted that "The Federal Government . . . has been reluctant to invest the funds needed to control the pollution which its activities create. In addition, Federal agencies have not been active in requiring people who do business with the Government to meet water quality requirements."[14] The proposed Water Quality Improvement Act establishes a mechanism for ensuring the conformance of Federal licensees with water quality standards, but little has been done about air pollution from such sources, and more action could be taken to prevent both air and water pollution caused by the recipients of Federal grants and contracts.

THE PURPOSE OF FEDERAL ENFORCEMENT

Up to this point we have been discussing primarily the formal authority of the Federal government to enforce pollution controls. In order fully to understand the enforcement process it is now necessary to look behind the legal powers and examine the purposes for which these powers are used. Many critics and commentators have assumed that the sole purpose of Federal enforcement actions is to force polluters to cease their pollution through Federal legal action or the threat of such action. This is not, in fact, the case.

All pollution control agencies, whether they be Federal, state, or local, are forced to recognize that legal proceedings against individual polluters can never be the chief goal of a compliance program. Formal hearings and court action consume an extraordinary amount of time and manpower. The St. Joseph case, where the pollution had still not been controlled twelve years after the initiation of enforcement action, illustrates how long it can take to force compliance through legal action. Furthermore, the courts are not experts on pollution, and the outcome of a court case is always somewhat unpredictable. Once a case goes to the courts, the final decision is no longer in the hands of the pollution control agency. All available experience indicates that laws against pollution, like all other laws, must rest primarily on voluntary action if their purpose is to be achieved. In addition, no agency has the resources to prosecute more than a small fraction of the polluters.

The necessary dependence on voluntary compliance, however, should not obscure the fact that the degree of such compliance may depend upon the success of the control agency in carrying out legal prosecution. Lewis Fuller, director of the Los Angeles County air pollution control agency, has stated that "Reasonable discussion with polluters about remedial steps is important, but there has to be the knowledge that if they don't shape up, they're going to land in court as sure as God made little apples."[15] If the Federal government should decide to embark on large-scale enforcement against individual polluters it probably will have to take many more cases to court. It has not yet attempted such enforcement because control of particular pollution sources has been considered the province of state and local governments.

The Clean Air Act states: "That the prevention and control

of air pollution at its source is the primary responsibility of States and local governments," and there is a similar statement of policy in the Water Pollution Control Act.[16] This declaration of congressional policy is reinforced by the recognition that neither FWPCA nor NAPCA currently have the manpower to assume a major portion of the enforcement work themselves. They would have to place heavy reliance on state and local enforcement action even if the law were silent about the "primary responsibility" of the subnational levels.

Given the time and manpower necessary for legal enforcement action and the deference to state and local authorities, the primary purpose of Federal enforcement has been to prod the state and local control agencies into taking action. This has been done in three ways: the negotiations between Federal and non-Federal officials which precede and follow an enforcement action; Federal technical aid in pinpointing the problems and their solution; and the mobilizing of public opinion to demand that the state and local agencies take action.

There is some conflict between the technique of negotiating with the relevant non-Federal officials and the attempt to mobilize public opinion. It is difficult to publicize the existence of pollution without also implicitly criticizing the efforts of state and local officials and thus provoking the resentment of such officials at the Federal intervention. The executive director of ORSANCO expressed this when he noted that

> The conference provision . . . was conceived [by the states] as offering a means through which the parties concerned could be brought together for resolving viewpoints prior to, and hopefully without the necessity of, formal proceedings to reach agreement on proposed federal compliance actions. Instead, the federal authorities elected to conduct the conferences virtually as public hearings, generally in the ballroom of a large hotel and with advance publicity geared to generate the attendance of hundreds of people. Furthermore, these conferences were shrouded with the atmosphere of an adversary proceeding, in which the federal representatives appeared to cast themselves as the savior of streams with the states in the role as opponents of such good intent."[17]

The general reliance on informal negotiations rather than

legal proceedings can be clearly seen from the pattern of enforcement activities which has emerged in both air and water pollution. In water pollution, of the forty-five enforcement conferences initiated, only four have gone to the public hearing stage. One of these four (Corney Creek) was called under the provisions of the 1948 act which provided for the hearing as the first step of enforcement procedures. The other three (Kansas City, Sioux City, and St. Joseph) were all on the Missouri River, the first major area tackled by FWPCA under the provisions of the 1956 act. Two of the Missouri hearings were held in 1959 and the third in 1960. Thus it has been ten years since FWPCA has proceeded to the public hearing stage. It seems evident that the experience gained in the early years of the water pollution control effort led to the conclusion that formal legal proceedings, represented by the public hearing, were not a productive method for achieving compliance.

The Federal air pollution agency was granted enforcement powers seven years after water pollution, and it therefore had the benefit of FWPCA's experience. NAPCA has, in effect, added a fourth stage to the enforcement process by holding extensive "consultations" with the state and local control agencies prior to the calling of a conference. Thus the informal on-the-record conference is preceded by informal off-the-record consultations. The first air pollution enforcement action has gone to the public hearing and court action stage, but the case is atypical in that it involves only a single polluter and was undertaken largely to establish the legal validity of the Clean Air Act. None of the other air pollution cases has gone beyond the conference stage.

In both air and water pollution enforcement the conference has come to be considered a continuing process rather than a discrete event. In most recent cases, it has not been terminated but simply adjourned, and in a number of cases the conference has been reconvened to consider the progress made in carrying out agreements reached at the first session. This procedure again emphasizes the basic character of the enforcement process as a setting for negotiations, and in most cases the negotiations are not with the polluters but with the state and local control agencies.

WATER POLLUTION—FEDERAL ENFORCEMENT EXPERIENCE

The forty-five enforcement actions undertaken by FWPCA have varied greatly in scope, ranging from situations involving only one or two polluters to a massive effort to reverse the deterioration of Lake Erie involving five states and hundreds of polluters. The choice of targets for enforcement actions has been determined by the seriousness of the problem in the area and by the possible political ramifications of initiating an enforcement case.

Enforcement is the most politically sensitive aspect of the Federal pollution control programs. The decision to call an enforcement conference represents the intrusion of the Federal government into an ongoing political situation. The existence of pollution in any particular state or locality represents a certain balance of particular forces (conservationists, industries, government officials, etc.), some of whom benefit from the status quo and some of whom want to change it. When the Federal forces enter the picture they inevitably change the balance to some extent and thus benefit certain interests and damage certain others. These interests usually include people such as governors, congressmen, or big-city mayors who can influence the Federal government. Thus, as a matter of self-preservation the pollution control agency must consider the likely political ramifications of undertaking an enforcement action.

The political ramifications must also be considered because they are crucial to the success or failure of the Federal effort to get the water cleaned up. The state and local political forces are usually in a position, if they so desire, to undermine any attempts to stop the pollution. The state legislature can override the decisions of the state or local pollution control agencies, a local mayor can delay almost indefinitely the installation of a waste treatment plant for his community, an influential Governor can use his power to accelerate or retard the pace at which industries install pollution control equipment. The political sensitivities of the state and local pollution control agencies must also be kept constantly in mind.

Given the political implications of enforcement, the Federal agencies in both air and water pollution control move cautiously before making the decision to call a conference. The choice of a particular area for action is always cleared by the relevant assistant secretary and, in the case of major actions, by the secretary of the department. Extensive consultations and elaborate stratagems often precede the decision. A major effort is often made to have the Governor of the state affected by the pollution "invite" the Federal government in, rather than have it appear that the Federal government unilaterally initiated the action.

Forty states have been involved in Federal water pollution enforcement actions. The major enforcement conferences have dealt with several areas of severe pollution along the Missouri River, with the Hudson, Potomac, Colorado, and Mississippi Rivers, and with the Great Lakes. Each of these actions has involved several states and a large number of polluting industries and municipalities. As might be expected from the large number of polluters and governmental jurisdictions involved, and from the negotiating character of the Federal enforcement process, progress toward achieving the recommendations of the abatement conference has been slow. No specific data showing progress are available, but none of the major enforcement actions has yet been formally concluded, which indicates that in no case have the recommendations been fully complied with.

It is too early to tell how the "streamlined" procedures for enforcing water quality standards will affect the enforcement process. The recommendations made by past enforcement conferences have been incorporated into the state water quality standards, and the number one priority in future years will undoubtedly be enforcement of the new standards. The majority of enforcement actions thus may be carried out under the new procedure, which eliminates both the conference and the public hearing. However, it is also likely that the real effect of the new procedure will be simply to make the conference stage completely informal and invisible to the general public.[18] Negotiations with the state and local control agencies and with the polluters will still take place, either before or after notice of violation of the standards is given.

"Notices" to polluters will probably be used more frequently than the public hearing mechanism because the establishment of the standards in itself constitutes a preliminary warning to those who are violating them, and thus the Federal government will feel less restraint in seeking court action against the recalcitrant. The establishment of the standards also · represents agreement between the Federal government and the states as to what constitutes desirable water quality, an issue which before 1967 consumed much of the time of the conferences and the negotiations which accompanied them.

AIR POLLUTION—FEDERAL ENFORCEMENT EXPERIENCE

HEW was given the power to conduct enforcement proceedings in the 1963 Clean Air Act. Since then eight enforcement conferences have been held. All except one of the conferences has dealt with interstate air pollution, the one exception being a request by the Governor of Montana for Federal assistance to alleviate an acute fluoride pollution problem arising from a phosphate processing plant in Powell County. Montana was in the process of passing its first major air pollution statute, and thus there would have been considerable delay before the state could have acted to curb the pollution.

Four of the enforcement conferences have dealt with single sources of pollution: a rendering plant in Delaware; pulp mills in Ticonderoga, New York, and Lewiston, Idaho; and the Montana phosphate plant noted above. Each of the other four conferences has considered all sources of pollution within major metropolitan areas: the New York-New Jersey metropolitan area; Kansas City, Kansas-Kansas City, Missouri; Parkersburg, West Virginia-Marietta, Ohio; and the Washington, D.C., metropolitan area.

The less-developed status of air pollution control at the state level has meant that the Federal impact on the state and local situation has been even greater than in water pollution. This is best indicated by the fact that in the recommendations stemming from enforcement cases dealing with entire metropolitan areas, HEW has included proposals dealing with the desirable organizational arrangements for controlling air pollution. Thus the first recommendation made by the New York-New Jersey conference was that, "In order to deal with the bi-state air pollution problem on a regional basis, an appropriate interstate agency must be vested with adequate legal authority," and the recommendation then spelled out the form which such an agency should take.[19]

The organizational recommendations made by the Federal enforcement conferences in many ways anticipated the provisions of the 1967 Air Quality Act. The areas covered by the New York and Washington enforcement conferences were identical to the areas which were later designated as air quality control regions under the 1967 act. The recommendations that uniform air quality standards be established for each region and that organizational machinery for enforcing such standards be established became requirements under the 1967 act. It is still too early to tell what the impact of the Air Quality Act on the enforcement process will be, but in those metropolitan areas where enforcement conferences have already been held, compliance with the provisions of the new act will involve essentially the same tasks as compliance with the conference recommendations.

PREVENTIVE ACTION

Compliance must rely primarily on voluntary action, and it is equally important that the voluntary compliance eventually take the form of preventing pollution before it occurs rather than stopping it once it has happened. Only through preventive action can there be any hope of achieving and maintaining the goal of clean air and water.

The establishment of standards is the most essential step in preventing pollution. If industries building new plants or municipalities building treatment facilities know in advance the level of treatment which must be given to wastes, then the design of the plant can take pollution control into account. Without standards it is a matter of chance whether or not a new plant or facility will pollute the air or water.

Many municipalities employ a system of permits to ensure that new construction will comply with pollution regulations. Permits are an effective tool, but they are only as good as the standards they are designed to implement.

Planning and zoning controls can also be used effectively to prevent both air and water pollution.[20] More research needs to be done on ways in which planning techniques can be utilized; in addition, there are currently severe political limitations on the use of planning and zoning. Control over the location of industries is one obvious way of ameliorating or preventing pollution. An HEW simulation study on sulfur oxides pollution concluded that "The abatement achieved by the relocation of the power plants is substantial and the annual costs of achieving abatement by this technique, under the assumptions set forth herein, indicate that it may be the least expensive technique for control of power plant emissions."[21] However, given the political weakness of local planning boards and the patchwork nature of local jurisdictions, a rational allocation of industrial sites in a metropolitan area is almost impossible. The struggle of many communities to obtain industry is also a severe constraint on planning efforts.

The compliance effort is today in a transitional stage. The next few years will indicate whether the Air and Water Quality Acts can bring about a significant improvement in environmental quality or whether still stronger efforts are needed. The new acts give the Federal government the tools for direct Federal enforcement against individual polluters, and, if the states and localities prove inadequate to the task, compliance will become increasingly a Federal function.

CHAPTER 9

Goals and the Policy Process

FOR THE PAST several years the public has been subjected to a constant barrage of apocalyptic statements on the dangers of pollution. How valid are such warnings? How much danger is there? Are we making any progress in controlling pollution? The simple answer to these questions is that nobody knows. The question of progress is difficult to answer because of the lack of reliable data and because of the differences between geographical areas. Some rivers are cleaner than they were ten years ago and some are dirtier, but there are no overall figures to indicate how the nation as a whole is doing. The government has recently issued figures showing that air pollution has increased from 133 million tons of contaminants in 1966 to 142 million tons in 1968,[1] but the reliability of these figures is open to question and gross weight is a very rough indicator of the air pollution problem.

Progress is an elusive concept when we are dealing with a problem whose nature and parameters are changing rapidly. Even if we were controlling those pollutants which we now believe are dangerous, there are many more whose effects are still unknown. The rapid growth of modern technology has not only hampered progress in pollution control but has also made imperative the need for a systematic approach to discovering the effects of particular substances. Each year hundreds of new chemical compounds and new uses for existing chemicals and metals are being introduced in the United States. And this is done with little regard for their effects on human health or on ecology.

We must begin to weigh the costs and benefits of technological innovation, and the government must assume the responsibility for identifying new problems and dangers and for balancing the risks against the benefits. However, the Federal government is currently not organized to perform such tasks, and there must be a new way of looking at pollution problems if we are to anticipate and prevent disasters rather than investigate them after they have occurred.

ORGANIZATION FOR POLLUTION CONTROL

Two basic points must be clarified in considering any proposed changes in the Federal government's organizational arrangements for controlling pollution. First, we must ask the extent to which air and water pollution are a single unified problem. Second, we must examine the goals of pollution control. The two are closely interrelated.

Of the many aspects common to air and water pollution, perhaps the most important is that people tend to perceive the two problems as similar. The semantics of the issues are sufficient to indicate this. We talk of "the pollution problem," and tend to consider air and water pollution as subcategories of a generic problem called "pollution."

The perception of a unified issue is not limited to semantics. The legislative history indicates quite clearly that those responsible for formulating air and water pollution laws have considered the same approaches and techniques applicable to both issues. The legislative provisions for standard-setting and enforcement to control water pollution were adopted almost without change for air pollution.

In recent years there has been an increasing number of proposals directed at unifying or at least coordinating all pollution control efforts. Several of the states have combined air and water pollution control functions in one agency. The Federal government now has a Council on Environmental Quality to consider environmental problems as a unified whole.

The perception of pollution as a single issue is closely related to the fact that the policymakers for air and water pollution have similar constituencies. The same interest groups are concerned with both issues, and concern with one issue is likely to lead a group into concern with the other. The pro-control alliance between municipalities and conservationists applies to air and water pollution. Most of the conservation groups began with a concern for water pollution control, but they have devoted increasing attention to the air pollution problem. The same industrial groups tend to be affected by air and water pollution control efforts, and their attitudes toward one issue carry over to the other. For example, industries such as chemicals, paper, and steel which depend on clean water for processing purposes probably take a somewhat more liberal attitude toward air pollution control than industries which can see no benefit from any form of pollution control.

Despite the similarities between air and water pollution control, however, there are also major differences. Water pollution can be controlled by construction of a public facility (a waste treatment plant and its connecting system of sewers, or a water purification plant) and it can be controlled after the pollutants have entered the water. These characteristics do not hold true for air pollution. While a technology for centrally treating air pollution is conceivable, it is not likely to be developed and applied at any time in the foreseeable future. Control of air pollution must take place before the pollutants enter the air, and this means that control action must be taken at each separate pollution source.

The implications of this difference are very great. They mean that much more of the effort and expenditure to control air pollution must come from the private sector than is the case in water pollution. They mean that in water pollution the government can offer some kind of service, namely, centralized treatment, but that in air pollution the government is almost exclusively a regulator and coercer. And they mean that scarcity of public funds is perhaps the major problem in controlling water pollution, whereas in air pollution political power to enforce regulations and the degree of voluntary compliance will be the deciding factors.

Another significant difference between air and water pollution concerns the logical geographic area for which control measures should be planned and applied. Planning and enforcement can be carried out most efficiently and effectively when done on the basis of the total area affected by the problem. In this way the sources of pollution and the persons and things affected by them will be brought under the same jurisdiction, and externalities will be avoided. For water pollution the logical area is a river basin. For air pollution the logical area is an airshed, which generally means a metropolitan area and the counties surrounding it. There are almost no cases where the boundaries of a river basin and an airshed come even close to coinciding.

We have been dealing so far with similarities and differences in the process of controlling air and water pollution. However, some of the most important differences involve not the control process itself but the benefits to be derived from successful control. What are the goals of air and water pollution control? If we try to calculate the costs and benefits of pollution control, what are the most important benefits? What is the proper context in which to consider air and water pollution?

Almost all pollution control programs were originally undertaken to protect public health. The effort to curb water pollution began with the fear of typhoid and other waterborne diseases. Concern with air pollution was spurred by such health disasters as the 1948 incident at Donora and the "killer smogs" in London and New York.

Air pollution control has retained its primary concern with health. Jurisdiction over the program has remained with the health agencies of the Federal government and the majority of states. The program has been sold to the public on the basis of protecting public health, and although damage to agriculture, materials, etc., receives some attention, the primary basis of enforcement and standard-setting decisions has been the effect of air pollutants on human health.

Water pollution control has become progressively less concerned with health problems. At the Federal level, FWPCA does not even have jurisdiction over the health effects of water pollution, this responsibility having been retained by HEW under the terms of the 1966 reorganization plan.[2]

The major benefits of the current water pollution control program are increased opportunities for recreation and the aesthetic satisfaction of clean water.[3] Both of these goals are important, particularly in a society enjoying an increasing amount of wealth and leisure time. However, an examination is needed of *who* in the society needs *what kinds* of recreational opportunities most, for we may discover that controlling water pollution should have lower priority from the standpoint of recreation than such alternatives as increasing open space in metropolitan areas or building swimming pools. As for aesthetics, we should not forget Mason Gaffney's reminder that

> The environment of slum dwellers consists largely of houses and streets, joints and cheap stores, playgrounds and schools, garbage cans and vibrations from neighborhood drop-forges. Perhaps it would be well to attend more to such more intimate urban environmental matters. Ameliorating them can improve the lot of man by a larger factor than cleaning up lakes used by summer sportsmen of the wealthier classes or improving the scenery on which they occasionally gaze with cultivated eyes.[4]

Since its transfer to the Department of the Interior, FWPCA has placed somewhat more emphasis on ecological concerns. Such factors were not until now considered a major benefit of the program because of our lack of knowledge of the effects of water pollutants on the natural environment. However, given the potential danger to the environment, the major justification for the water pollution program and the major basis for decisionmaking within it must be the prevention of ecological disaster.

The value of pollution control thus rests primarily on its contribution to health and ecology. These goals serve as a logical basis for the establishment of environmental standards, and make more sense organizationally than the current division between air and water pollution. The current division is convenient from the standpoint of actually controlling pollution, since the control areas, the control technology, and the political problems of control tend to be different for the two types of pollution; but it does not make sense in relation to the *goals* of control, especially that of health.

The central focus of environmental health should be how

much of any given substance a human being is exposed to. It is immaterial for the person's health whether the exposure comes through air, water, food, drugs, soil, or any other medium. This is implicitly recognized in relation to radioactive substances and pesticides, which are now dealt with separately from the air and water pollution programs at the Federal level. Radiation and pesticides are not unique, but typical. The major health hazard today comes from the hundreds of metals and thousands of chemicals which find their way into air, water, and soil. We do not know how much human exposure to these substances come through ,each of the various media, but we do know that it comes through all of them to some extent. We cannot look at them solely as air pollutants or water pollutants.

The dangers posed by chemicals and metals represent a vast, unexplored set of problems. Although we may have begun to make some progress in controlling the traditional air and water pollutants, we have not yet faced the task of coping with the "new" pollutants. For example, there is a metal called cadmium used in . many manufacturing processes, found in certain kinds of foods, and also present in most polluted urban atmospheres. Recent investigations have shown that: (1) People who die of heart disease have significantly higher amounts of cadmium in their bodies than those who die from other causes; (2) areas of the world in which people eat diets high in cadmium have higher heart-disease rates than other areas of the world; (3) in repeated laboratory experiments, rats exposed to cadmium developed heart disease. In short, there is sufficient scientific evidence to identify cadmium as at least a contributing cause of heart disease.[5]

These discoveries about cadmium were not made by a governmental agency. There is no agency of the Federal government with the responsibility for investigating the effects of such substances. Nothing is being done to control the introduction of cadmium into the environment. Several agencies—the Food and Drug Administration and NAPCA, for examples—have some control powers, but no agency exists to coordinate such efforts and there are large gaps in coverage. Nobody knows what the major sources of cadmium entering the environment are or how much of the metal is being put into the environment. And there is no Federal agency with the responsibility for developing this information.[6]

The example of cadmium could be repeated for many other substances; how many we do not know. What is needed is a Federal agency with responsibility for determining the health effects of all such substances, setting standards for human exposure to them, registering and approving new chemicals, and monitoring the course of such substances in the environment, thus tracing the sources of human exposure.[7] The establishment of such an agency is the only way in which we can begin to discover and control the effects of modern technology.

The ecological dangers of pollution may be as immediate and pressing as the health dangers. Just as in the health field, we need to know much more than we now do. And such facts as the steady accumulation of carbon dioxide in the atmosphere and the accumulation of pesticides in the bodies of animals indicate that we need to acquire the knowledge rapidly. A comprehensive approach to ecological understanding and action is required at the Federal level.

The existing air pollution program could well serve as the basis for building a comprehensive environmental health agency. The existing water pollution program could serve as the basis for a comprehensive ecology agency. The actual control of the different kinds of pollution could remain separated, but there is an immediate need to overcome the air-water distinction so far as monitoring, research, and standard-setting are concerned.

Changes in organization and perspective are necessary, but they will not by themselves eliminate any pollution. Let us now review the air and water pollution political system in order to explore the other changes which will be needed if we are to make further progress toward clean air and water.

THE PACE OF POLLUTION CONTROL

The general pace of pollution control in the United States is now governed by the actions of the Federal government.

Federal legislation sets the framework and the agenda for state and local action. Federal research determines what the priority problems are and what the standards should be. Federal appropriations for waste treatment grants are the major influence on the rate of construction of water pollution control facilities.

The Congress and the President determine the direction and pace of Federal efforts. The major pollution control legislation over the past five years has been largely the handiwork of Senator Muskie, and there is no reason to believe that this will change even with a Republican in the White House. The congressional dominance in the legislative field will be maintained. However, the President has the power to stimulate the Congress into taking action on new legislation or to veto proposals with which he is in strong disagreement.

The President also has the dominant voice in how much money is appropriated for pollution control. Given the overriding issues of Vietnam and inflation, it is impossible to predict whether large increases in the pollution budgets will occur. But it can safely be predicted that the water pollution effort will not proceed at a rapid pace until more Federal funds become available.

The ability of the President to publicize an issue should not be neglected. Public opinion forms the backdrop and sets the limits within which the specific legislative and budgetary actions take place. In the past, the course of events in pollution has been strongly influenced by some dramatic event (Donora, the New York smog, the Santa Barbara oil spill) being translated by the President into a directive for government action. Such events are likely to occur again in the future, and the focus and direction of pollution control may be greatly determined by how and whether the President capitalizes on them to move the government.

STANDARD-SETTING

Although the general pace and framework of pollution control are set by the President and Congress, the "gut" issues of standard-setting and compliance will determine the degree to which pollution is actually controlled. The effectiveness of standards and compliance depends partially on the general pace and direction of the programs. But adequate legislative authority, sufficient funds, and the backing of public opinion will have little real effect unless translated into adequate standards and compliance in the actual locations where pollution occurs.

The scientific basis for pollution control standards is woefully inadequate. We do not know the effects of most pollutants on human health, on plants and animals, or on anything else. It is one of the major characteristics of pollution politics that decisions are made in the context of a serious lack of knowledge about the effects of existing pollution and about the costs and benefits of any improvement in the existing situation. This ignorance increases the importance of public opinion and interest group influence. Power, rhetoric, and instinct must substitute for knowledge.

The need for more knowledge about the effects of pollution is obvious, but it should not obscure recognition of the nonscientific component in setting standards. Science cannot, by its very nature, tell us what should be. Only by combining our limited knowledge with our ethical and political judgments can we arrive at decisions as to what action to take. Only by being clear about what we know and don't know, and about what decisions must be made through the political process, can we arrive at defensible standards for pollution control.

THE PROBLEMS OF COMPLIANCE

Compliance with pollution standards depends on a large number of factors, both governmental and nongovernmental. The major responsibility for enforcement rests with state and local governments. But local governments are often themselves major polluters, and the cleaning up of our air and water requires not only local enforcement but local willingness to spend the funds required to eliminate municipal pollution. The cooperation of the private sector is also necessary. No matter how vigorous governmental enforcement efforts are, if there is not a high degree of voluntary compliance on the part of industry the pollution control effort is doomed to failure. Given the large number of governments and firms which in effect have a veto power over control efforts, compliance is the most vulnerable part of the pollution control process, the stage at which failure is most likely. Of course, compliance is also the stage which has the most impact on the interests of concerned parties. It does not cost anybody anything to write good laws or set stringent standards if the laws and standards are not to be enforced.

The problems of achieving compliance have led to a consideration of methods other than the usual standards and enforcement approach. Tax incentives to industry for air pollution control would help to bring about a greater degree of compliance. Federal funds for water pollution treatment plants are often a form of subsidy to industry since industrial firms frequently discharge their wastes into a municipal plant.[8] The private firm will pay a lower charge for use of the municipal facility if part of the costs of building the facility are paid by the Federal government. There is no equivalent subsidy in air pollution, and yet such a "bribe" to the private sector is more important in controlling air pollution because of the need to control air pollutants at the emission source. Some form of Federal tax incentive for air pollution control should be provided.[9]

We have discussed the idea of imposing effluent fees or some similar kind of substitute for the market mechanism. It should be kept in mind that an effluent fee scheme would not change the political forces involved in compliance but would simply change the ground rules under which they operate. In trying to predict the effects of such a change we are handicapped by lack of any detailed knowledge about the politics of compliance at the state and local level. This should be a priority area for social science research. Even if such research were done, however, prediction would still be difficult, and the only way ultimately to determine the effectiveness of the fee mechanism is to try it out. We need to experiment with all types of economic penalties.

Federal enforcement efforts up to now have been directed primarily at stimulating state and local governments to take action. If compliance continues at an unsatisfactory pace, however, there will be increased pressure for direct Federal enforcement against polluters. The mechanism for such direct enforcement already exists under the streamlined procedures contained in the Water Quality and Air Quality Acts. Whether it will be used depends on the future of intergovernmental relations in controlling pollution.

INTERGOVERNMENTAL RELATIONS

The history of pollution control over the past twenty years has been a history of increasing assumption of power and responsibility by the Federal government. There is every indication that this trend will continue.

Although there are no good measurements to prove or disprove the assertion, there exists widespread agreement that the states and localities have not done an adequate job of controlling pollution. Dissatisfaction with the pace of control at the local level has been one of the prime forces responsible for Washington's increased influence. There is no reason to believe that this view will change. It will in fact be reinforced by growing public anger at instances of local pollution and by dramatic events which catch the attention of the entire nation. Each fishkill, each oil spillage, each air pollution warning for a major city will increase the demand for a stronger Federal effort.

The demand for national action is not an illogical appeal to the court of last resort. The Federal government is superior to the states and localities in that it possesses the triumvirate of resources—money, knowledge, and power—necessary to achieve clean air and water. Federal financial resources will be required to meet the very high costs of pollution control. Only the Federal government has the scientific and technical personnel needed to develop the body of knowledge necessary to set air and water quality standards. Federal power is superior both because it is not subject to the jurisdictional limits of states and localities and because Washington has proven less vulnerable to the pressures of industrial polluters.

For the next few years we will be going through a trial period to test the effectiveness of the joint Federal-state mechanism for setting standards. In water pollution, the process laid down by the 1965 act has resulted in standards being approved for all fifty states. However, there will continue to be a need for planning and control for entire river basins, and this will be difficult to meet on any kind of state basis. Both in water and air pollution control, successful regional organization will only be accomplished if the Federal government plays an active and continuous role in the organizations' work, and perhaps only if the organizations are actually Federal bodies.

The crucial test of the regional concept is contained in the standard-setting and enforcement procedures of the 1967 Air Quality Act. This presents a more difficult test for states to meet than does the Water Quality Act, and it also lays down more clearly the path for direct Federal intervention if the states are unsuccessful. Given past experience in state cooperation and the lack of state experience in air pollution control, it is likely that Washington will eventually have to follow the path of intervention.

The pressures for regional cooperation established by the Air Quality Act may indeed enable the Federal government to play a constructive role in fostering interstate cooperation. The establishment of interstate compacts is time-consuming and cumbersome, and a more flexible arrangement is needed. Given the Federal powers under the Air Quality Act, HEW may be able to establish new forms of Federal-interstate cooperation which would be applicable to other functional areas. Federal intervention could take the form of joint Federal-state use of Federal powers for the accomplishment of common ends.

Emissions from automobiles, the number one source of air pollution, are now subject to Federal standards. Not only will these standards have to be made more stringent, but Federal research will have to be used as a weapon to force the automobile industry into modification or perhaps abandonment of the internal combustion engine. The same kind of Federal authority may also have to be employed in controlling air pollution from certain major industries such as steel, chemicals, and power generation. A proposal to this effect was contained in the administration's version of the 1967 act. It was struck from the bill by Muskie's committee, but will undoubtedly be made again in future years.

As pollution becomes a worldwide problem, a new dimension will be added to the Federal government's role. Water pollution from oil and vessels is already a problem with significant international consequences. Dr. Morris Neiburger, Professor of Meteorology at UCLA, has stated that "The [air] pollution levels at any one place are determined not by the local sources alone, but by the contributions of sources at large distances, and in the future they may be significantly affected by all sources throughout the world." [10] And the Secretary General of the United Nations noted in a recent report that "damage to the human environment is creating a crisis of worldwide importance. . . . No nation can any longer be isolated from these global pressures." [11] The need for nations to cooperate in protecting the world environment will become increasingly pressing in future years.

The above predictions of greater Federal power should not be taken to mean that states and localities will cease to be important factors in the politics of pollution. State and local governments are firmly imbedded in the American political system. Pollution control has and will continue to have significant effects on local expenditures, industrial location, and other matters of great significance to local governments, and these governments will not hesitate to use their political resources to protect their interests. Federal policy will therefore have to be formulated and carried out within the restraints provided by active and powerful local governments.

The states and localities represent not only restraints but also opportunities. Enforcement efforts will probably continue to rely heavily on state and local action. Even more important in the long run will be actions taken by the local governments to prevent pollution before it occurs. We cannot hope to achieve clean air and water until we can ensure that new housing and industry will be pollution-free. This is a task for states and localities. The kinds of powers needed—certification and permit granting, promulgation of zoning and building codes, and inspection for compliance—are local powers. If the states and localities can accomplish this, we shall be much closer to achieving a satisfactory environment.

The weighing of costs and benefits cannot be avoided in the compliance effort because priorities must be set and we must know how much emphasis to place on the control of each kind of pollution. This can only be done through greater knowledge of the effects of the various pollutants, and the search for such knowledge must be based on a comprehensive system if we are to deal successfully with the rapid pace of technological innovation. We cannot continue to use the entire population as guinea pigs or the entire environment as a laboratory, because if we are wrong in our haphazard calculations of the costs it may be too late to rectify the mistake. We also cannot stop all the activities which introduce potentially dangerous substances into the environment, because to do so would be to sacrifice most of the benefits of modern society. We must find out the effects of potential pollutants so that we can avoid disaster and at the same time improve rather than impoverish our lives.

All the ignorance and uncertainty should not be allowed to obscure the fact that it is within our ability now to control much, perhaps most, of the gross pollution which exists. We can build the treatment plants and install the control devices if the political system decides that it is important enough to do so. This is a matter of money and political power, and of the two power is the more important.

Notes

CHAPTER 1

1. On the severe limitations of cost-benefit analysis in pollution control, see J. H. Dales, *Pollution, Property and Prices* (Toronto: University of Toronto Press, 1968), Chaps. 3 and 4.
2. *U.S. News and World Report,* April 3, 1967, pp. 42–45.
3. See U.S. Dept. of the Interior, FWPCA, "Manpower and Training Needs in Water Pollution Control," Document 49, U.S. Senate (90th Congress, 1st session); and Air Pollution Control Association, "Report of the Education and Training Committee," *Journal of the Air Pollution Control Association,* XVI:11 (1966), pp. 610–613.
4. For a somewhat similar view of the development of environmental quality issues, see U.S. House of Representatives, Committee on Science and Astronautics, Subcommittee on Science, Research, and Development, "Managing the Environment" (1968), pp. 9–12.
5. See Earl Finbar Murphy, *Water Purity* (Madison, Wis.: University of Wisconsin Press, 1961), p. 55, and *Governing Nature* (Chicago: Quadrangle Books, 1967), p. 121.
6. U.S. Dept. of the Interior, "The Federal Water Pollution Control Program," (Washington, D.C.: GPO, December 2, 1968), p. 4.
7. Death rates per 100,000 population from typhoid were as follows: 1900–31.3; 1910–22.5; 1920–7.6; 1930–4.8; 1940–1.1; 1956–0.0. U.S. Dept. of Commerce, Bureau of the Census, *Historical Statistics of the U.S.: Colonial Times to 1957* (Washington, D.C.: GPO, 1960), series B 114–128, p. 26.
8. Ralph C. Williams, *The United States Public Health Service 1798–1950* (Washington, D.C.: The Commissioned Officers Association of the U.S. Public Health Service, 1951), p. 312.
9. *Ibid.* The statute is the Public Health Service Act, P.L. 78-410.
10. *Ibid.,* pp. 312–313.

11. See Leon Weinberger, *et al.,* "Solving Our Water Problems—Water Renovation and Reuse,". *Annals of the New York Academy of Sciences,* Vol. 136, art. 5 (July 8, 1966), p. 138.

12. S. R. Weibel, *et al.,* "Waterborne Disease Outbreaks from 1946 to 1960" (Cincinnati, Ohio: U.S. Public Health Service, February 1964).

13. FWPCA, "The Cost of Clean Water and Its Economic Impact," (January 10, 1969), Vol. 1, p. 6; Vol. 2, p. 12; and FWPCA, "Problems of Combined Sewer Facilities and Overflows" (December 1, 1967), p. 9. The Dept. of Housing and Urban Development estimates that 93 per cent of new residential construction is served by sewerage systems. Letter to the author from S. Porter Driscoll, Director, Architectural Division, Dept. of Housing and Urban Development, Federal Housing Administration, July 11, 1969.

14. FWPCA, "The Cost of Clean Water and Its Economic Impact," *op. cit.,* Vol. 1, p. 134.

15. See FWPCA, "The Cost of Clean Water," (January 10, 1968), Vol. 1, pp. 20–21.

16. *Ibid.,* p. 36.

17. See "Federal Agency Is Accused of Laxity in Control of Pesticides," *New York Times,* September 17, 1968, 24:3.

18. See Sheldon Novick, *The Careless Atom* (Boston: Houghton Mifflin, 1968), and U.S. Congress, Joint Committee on Atomic Energy, "Selected Materials on Environmental Effects of Producing Electric Power" (Washington, D.C.: GPO, August 1969).

19. U.S. Senate, Committee on Public Works, Subcommittee on Air and Water Pollution, "Water Pollution—1967" (Washington, D.C.: GPO, 1967), part 1, p. 322.

20. Some of the states, notably Pennsylvania, have initiated control programs. For a general review of the problem and what is being done about it, see *ibid.,* pp. 313–422.

21. *New York Times,* March 3, 1969, quoted in U.S. Congress, "Selected Materials on Environmental Effects of Producing Electric Power," *op. cit.,* p. 377. Nuclear power capacity is estimated to grow from 2.7m kilowatts in 1968 to 150m Kw. in 1980 and to 941m Kw. in 2000; *ibid.,* p. 26.

22. Remarks by Max N. Edwards, Assistant Secretary of the Interior for Water Pollution Control, before the National Resources and Public Utilities Sections of the annual, meeting of the American Bar Association, Philadelphia, Pa., August 6, 1968, p. 1.

23. FWPCA, "The Cost of Clean Water and Its Economic Impact," *op. cit.,* Vol. 1, p. 158. See also Burt Schorr, "Generating Plants Pose a 'Thermal Pollution' Threat to Rivers, Lakes," *Wall Street Journal,* December 1, 1967, 1:6.

24. Secretary of the Interior and the Secretary of Transportation, "Oil Pollution—A Report to the President" (Washington, D.C.: GPO, February 1968), p. 10.

25. *Ibid.,* p. 13.
26. See Murphy, *Governing Nature,* pp. 60–64.
27. U.S. Senate, "Water Pollution–1967," *op. cit.,* part 1, p. 448.
28. *Ibid.,* pp. 451–452.
29. Jack Bregman and Sergei Lenormond, *The Pollution Paradox* (New York: Spartan Books, 1966), p. 6.
30. National Academy of Sciences–National Research Council, "Waste Management and Control" (Washington, D.C., 1966), p. 11.
31. (Boston: Houghton Mifflin, 1962).
32. Federal Security Administration, Public Health Service, press release, October 14, 1949.
33. U.S. Senate, Committee on Public Works, Subcommittee on Air and Water Pollution, "Air Pollution–1967" (Washington, D.C.: GPO, 1967), part 2, p. 793.
34. See U.S. House of Representatives, Committee on Government Operations, "Federal Air Pollution Research and Development: An Interim Report on Sulfur Oxides Pollution Abatement R and D," House Report 91-79 (91st Congress, 1st session), March 13, 1969, pp. 7–8.
35. See U.S. Senate, "Air Pollution–1967," part 2, p. 821.
36. *Ibid.,* p. 805.

CHAPTER 2

1. For more detailed analyses of legislative events through 1966, see M. Kent Jennings, "Legislative Politics and Water Pollution Control 1956-1961," in Frederic N. Cleaveland, and associates, *Congress and Urban Problems* (Washington, D.C.: The Brookings Institution, 1969); James L. Sundquist, *Politics and Policy: The Eisenhower, Kennedy, and Johnson Years* (Washington, D.C.: The Brookings Institution, 1968), pp. 322–381; and U.S. House of Representatives, Committee on Science and Astronautics, "Technical Information for Congress," April 25, 1969, pp. 337–356.
2. Rivers and Harbors Act, 30 Stat. 1152.
3. The Oil Pollution Act, 1924, 33 U.S.C. 431, *et seq.*
4. In 1934 Roosevelt appointed a special advisory committee of the U.S. National Resources Committee to report to him on the problem of water pollution. It reported in 1935 that pollution abatement was a local responsibility, but that the Federal government should provide loans or grants to public agencies and loans to non-public agencies for the construction of treatment works. See U.S. Senate, Select Committee on National Water Resources, "Reviews of National Water Resources During the Past Fifty Years" (Washington, D.C.: GPO, 1959), Committee Print No. 2.
5. For a discussion of the major issues involved, see Herman G. Baity, "Aspects of Governmental Policy on Stream Pollution Abate-

ment," *American Journal of Public Health,* XXIX:12 (December 1939), pp. 1297–1307.

6. HR 12764, 74th Congress.

7. HR 2711, 75th Congress.

8. See *Congressional Record,* Vol. 83, part 8 (75th Congress, 3rd session), p. 9710.

9. S.685, 76th Congress.

10. P.L. 82-579.

11. U.S. House of Representatives, Committee on Appropriations, Report 228 (84th Congress, 1st session), p. 11.

12. See "Report of the Joint Federal-State Action Committee to the President of the U.S. and the Chairman of the Governor's Conference" (Washington, D.C.: Progress Report 1, filed December 1957, publ. 1958).

13. HR 3610, 86th Congress.

14. For the compromises which produced these proposals see Sundquist, *op. cit.,* p. 350.

15. See Robert Engler, *The Politics of Oil* (Chicago: University of Chicago Press, 1961).

16. See *New York Times,* April 16, 1967, 41:1. Wright later denied that he had submitted the amendment.

17. See "Report on International Control of Oil Pollution," House Report 628 (90th Congress, 1st session), September 11, 1967; Edward Cowan, *Oil and Water* (Philadelphia: Lippincott, 1968); and Richard Petrow, *In the Wake of Torrey Canyon* (New York: McKay, 1968).

18. S.2525, 90th Congress, sec. 2.

19. *1968 Congressional Quarterly Almanac* (Washington, D.C.: Congressional Quarterly Service, 1969), p. 569.

20. The financing provisions were not included because the new administration was working on its own version of a financing bill. The new bill was submitted in July 1969, as HR 12913.

21. For a more detailed analysis of legislative events through 1966, see Randall B. Ripley, "Congress and Clean Air," in Cleaveland, and associates, *op. cit.;* and Sundquist, *op. cit.,* pp. 322–381.

22. See Ripley, *op. cit.,* pp. 229–230.

23. Memorandum from the Secretary of HEW to Senator Chavez, April 18, 1955.

24. Memorandum from Alex Greene to William Carey, April 30, 1955, Bureau of the Budget files.

25. P.L. 86-365.

26. *Public Papers of the Presidents of the U.S.: John F. Kennedy— 1961* (Washington, D.C.: GPO, 1962), p. 117.

27. P.L. 87-761.

28. *Public Papers of the Presidents of the U.S.: John F. Kennedy— 1963* (Washington, D.C.: GPO, 1964), p. 145.

29. P.L. 86-493.

30. This account relies heavily on Sundquist, *op. cit.,* pp. 369–371.

31. "Proceedings: The Third National Conference on Air Pollution" (Washington, D.C.: GPO, 1967), pp. 14–15.

32. *Ibid.,* p. 597.

CHAPTER 3

1. Richard Neustadt, "Presidency and Legislation: Planning the President's Program," *American Political Science Review,* XLIX:4 (December 1955), p. 1015.

2. See Ripley, "Congress and Clean Air," *op. cit.,* p. 241 and p. 244.

3. See Theodore Sorensen, *Kennedy* (New York: Bantam Books, 1966), p. 265.

4. *Ibid.,* p. 267.

5. For a further discussion of the task forces, see Norman C. Thomas and Harold Wolman, "Policy Formulation in the Institutionalized Presidency: The Johnson Task Forces," in Thomas Cronin and Sanford Greenberg, *The Presidential Advisory System* (New York: Harper & Row, 1969).

6. Neustadt, *op. cit.,* p. 1013.

7. Sorensen, *op. cit.,* p. 266.

8. See Rowland Evans and Robert Novak, *Lyndon B. Johnson: The Exercise of Power* (New York: New American Library, 1966), pp. 201–202.

9. See Ripley, *op. cit.,* p. 259.

10. *Ibid., passim.*

11. See U.S. House of Representatives, Committee on Government Operations, "Federal Air Pollution R and D on Sulfur Oxides Pollution Abatement," September 5, 1968, and "Federal Air Pollution Research and Development: An Interim Report on Sulfur Oxides Pollution Abatement R and D," Report 91-79 (91st Congress, 1st session), March 13, 1969.

12. See U.S. House of Representatives, Committee on Science and Astronautics, Subcommittee on Science, Research and Development, "Environmental Pollution: A Challenge to Science and Technology" (1966) and "Managing the Environment" (1968).

13. "Managing the Environment," *op. cit.,* p. 8.

14. U.S. Senate, Committee on Interior and Insular Affairs, and U.S. House of Representatives, Committee on Science and Astronautics, "Congressional White Paper on a National Policy for the Environment" (October 1968).

15. The House version called for a five-member "Council of Environmental Quality."

16. Statement by Sen. Edmund S. Muskie in the U.S. Senate introducing the Environmental Quality Improvement Act of 1969, June 12, 1969, mimeo, p. 4.

17. See *Congressional Record,* October 8, 1969, pp. 12099–12160. Jackson commented during the debate that "this rather unusual procedure [of dealing with the two environmental quality bills] is, in part, the outgrowth of some basic and still unresolved questions relating to the jurisdictions of the standing committees of both Houses of the Congress on legislative matters relating to Federal policies on preserving and maintaining the quality of man's environment." *Ibid.,* pp. 12112–12113.

18. Unfortunately, the technical difficulties of determining the precise dollar amounts of presidential requests and congressional action in programs experiencing rapid legislative and organizational change have precluded any detailed analysis of congressional budgetary action.

19. See Richard F. Fenno, Jr., *The Power of the Purse* (Boston: Little, Brown, 1966), p. 686.

20. *Ibid.,* p. 366.

21. See *Congressional Record,* October 8, 1969, pp. H9224–9295; and *New York Times,* August 17, 1969, 40:1; September 29, 1969, 30:2; October 7, 1969, 19:1; and October 10, 1969, 1:7.

22. Cleaveland, and associates, *op. cit.,* p. 359.

23. *Ibid.,* pp. 356–357.

24. By "resolved" I mean only in the sense that a greater degree of stability will be established in such matters as agency jurisdiction.

CHAPTER 4

1. Ido de Groot, "Some Airy Platitudes About Attitudes—Trends in Public Attitudes Towards Air Pollution," Paper 67–71, 1967 Air Pollution Control Association Meeting, Cleveland, Ohio, p. 1.

2. See David Easton, *A Systems Analysis of Political Life* (New York: Wiley, 1965), Chaps. 3 and 5.

3. See Table 4–1.

4. See Table 4–2.

5. de Groot, *op. cit.,* p. 6.

6. J. Schusky, "Public Awareness and Concern with Air Pollution in the St. Louis Metropolitan Area" (Washington, D.C.: HEW, Public Health Service, May 1965), pp. 13–15.

7. de Groot, *op. cit.,* p. 7.

8. See Table 4–3.

9. FWPCA's 1968 funds for public relations were slightly over half a million dollars, and this figure does not include the value of free time and space donated by television and radio stations, newspapers, etc.

10. de Groot, *op. cit.,* pp. 8–9.

11. *New York Times,* February 8, 1968, 29:1.

12. *Washington Post,* April 3, 1967, 2:1.

13. *New York Times,* December 3, 1967, 28:1; *Newsweek,* October 6, 1969, p. 46.

14. See, for example, "The Citizen's Role in Air Pollution" (Washington, D.C.: GPO, 1967) and "What You Can Do About Water Pollution" (Washington, D.C.: GPO, 1967).

15. The correlation coefficient for the two rankings was $r' = .34$. The Spearman rank correlation coefficient was $K = 1.126$.

16. "Conservation Policies of the Izaak Walton League of America," as revised January 1, 1964, brochure, n.d., p. 9.

17. See Murphy, *Water Purity,* pp. 89–90.

18. "Major Conservation Issues, 1968," resolutions adopted at the 32nd annual convention of the National Wildlife Federation, Houston, Tex., March 8–10, 1968.

19. See League of Women Voters Education Fund, *The Big Water Fight* (Brattleboro, Vt.: Stephen Greene Press, 1966).

20. Ripley, "Congress and Clean Air," *op. cit.,* pp. 237–241.

21. National Tuberculosis Association, brochure, n.d.

22. See Harold M. England, "APCA: A Mission and a Method Through Sixty Years of Service," *Journal of the Air Pollution Control Association* (June 1967), pp. 371–373.

23. Study by McGraw-Hill Co. cited by Joe Moore, Jr., Commissioner, FWPCA, in remarks before the Water Pollution Control Federation, Chicago, Ill., September 24, 1968, p. 2. There exist several widely varying estimates for industry pollution control expenditures. The McGraw-Hill figures are probably on the high side.

24. FWPCA, "The Cost of Clean Water and Its Economic Impact," *op. cit.,* Vol. 1, pp. 144–145.

25. *Ibid.,* p. 146.

26. *Ibid.,* p. 150.

27. Twenty-three states have exempted pollution control equipment from property or other types of taxes. See J. F. Zimmerman, "Political Boundaries and Air Pollution Control" (Albany, N.Y.: Graduate School of Public Affairs, State University of New York, n.d.), p. 3.

28. Charles L. Schultze, *The Politics and Economics of Public Spending* (Washington, D.C.: The Brookings Institution, 1969), p. 122.

29. See "Cost Sharing with Industry?" (Washington, D.C.: Working Committee on Economic Incentives, Federal Coordinating Committee on the Economic Impact of Pollution Abatement, November 20, 1967); and ABT Associates, Inc., for FWPCA, "Incentives to Industry for Water Pollution Control: Policy Considerations" (Cambridge, Mass., December 1967).

30. See P.L. 89-800.

31. During the 90th Congress, in the House alone, 111 bills were introduced to provide some form of investment tax credit for industrial pollution control.

32. *New York Times,* June 18, 1969, 1:1.

33. For example, see E. J. Cleary, *The ORSANCO Story* (Baltimore: Johns Hopkins Press, 1967), pp. 96-97, where he discusses the role of General Electric; and the series of ads during 1968 and 1969 run in national magazines by the Standard Oil Co. of New Jersey.
34. See *New York Times,* January 11, 1969, 1:3; September 12, 1969, 1:2; and October 8, 1969, 30:3. The fact that the suit was initiated only ten days before the Johnson Administration left office probably indicates the reluctance of the administration to incur the wrath of the auto companies.
35. U.S. Senate, Committee on Public Works, Subcommittee on Air and Water Pollution, "Air Pollution—1968," part 1, p. 30 (statement of Fred E. Tucker).
36. I am indebted to Mr. Wendell Pigman for this information.
37. Merrill, Lynch, Pierce, Fenner and Smith, Inc., Securities Research Division, "Five Emerging Industries" (April 1968).

CHAPTER 5

1. See Federal Council for Science and Technology, Committee on Environmental Quality, "Noise—Sound Without Value" (Washington, D.C.: GPO, September 1968).
2. League of Women Voters, *The Big Water Fight,* Appendix A.
3. *Presidential Documents,* 3:16 (April 24, 1967), pp. 651-652.
4. For examples of this approach see Aerojet-General Corp., Von Karman Center, "California Waste Management Study" (Azusa, Calif., August 1965); and A. V. Kneese and R. C. d'Arge, "Pervasive External Costs and the Response of Society," in U.S. Congress, Joint Economic Committee, Subcommittee on Economy in Government, "The Analysis and Evaluation of Public Expenditures: The PPB System" (Washington, D.C.: GPO, 1969), Vol. 1, pp. 87-115.
5. Webster's Collegiate Dictionary, 5th ed.
6. *New York Times,* June 27, 1968, 42:2.
7. See *New York Times,* October 23, 1969, 49:5.
8. See Ripley, "Congress and Clean Air," *op. cit.,* p. 228.
9. *Ibid.*
10. See Fig. 5-1.
11. See Table 5-1.
12. U.S. House of Representatives, Committee on Appropriations, "Hearings on Dept. of the Interior and Related Agencies Appropriations for 1970" (1969), part 1, p. 258.
13. Williams, *The U.S. Public Health Service 1798-1950,* p. 312.
14. Murphy, *Water Purity,* p. 18.
15. Section 3(b) of the act did not specify the exact locations of the labs, but rather the general area of the country (Northeast, Middle Atlantic, etc.) for each of the seven. The seven locations later specified included one in the district of John Fogarty, chairman of the relevant House Appropriations Subcommittee; one in Okla-

homa, the home state of Senator Kerr, chairman of the Senate Rivers and Harbors Committee; and one in the district of John Blatnik, chairman of the House Rivers and Harbors Committee. Appropriations for construction of the labs were vehemently opposed by the Budget Bureau because of the injurious effect such decentralization would have on the water pollution research effort. The Bureau succeeded in preventing one lab from being built and delayed construction of the others.

16. See Wilbur Cohen, and J. Sonosky, "The Federal Water Pollution Control Act Amendments of 1961," *Public Health Reports* (February 1962).

17. See Sundquist, *op. cit.,* p. 330.

18. Reorganization Plan No. 2 of 1966.

19. The idea of transferring water pollution functions to Interior was not without congressional precedent. In 1963, Rep. Dingell, a major proponent of water pollution control, introduced legislation calling for such a transfer. See U.S. House of Representatives, Committee on Government Operations, "Water Pollution Control and Abatement" (May–June 1963; publ. 1964), part 1A, pp. 400–401.

20. See Table 5–2.

21. P.L. 89-80.

22. See Fig. 5–2.

23. P.L. 89-4.

24. P.L. 89-136.

25. P.L. 89-117.

26. P.L. 89-240.

27. See U.S. Senate, Committee on Appropriations, "Hearings on Public Works and AEC Appropriations, 1969," part 1, pp. 1630–1631.

28. See, for example, Richard Fenno, *The President's Cabinet* (Cambridge, Mass.: Harvard University Press, 1959); and U.S. Senate, Committee on Government Operations, Subcommittee on National Policy Machinery, "Organizing for National Security" (1961), Vol. 3.

29. *Presidential Documents,* 2:35 (September 5, 1966), pp. 1195–1197.

30. *Ibid.,* p. 1196.

31. Executive Order 11472, May 29, 1969.

32. National Environmental Policy Act of 1969, P.L. 91-190.

CHAPTER 6

1. See Constance McLaughlin Green, *The Rise of Urban America* (New York: Harper & Row, 1967), pp. 8, 25.

2. Murphy, *Water Purity,* pp. 65–66.

3. See Table 6–1.

4. See *New York Times,* February 9, 1969, 77:1.

5. As of October 1, 1968, twenty-one states had legislation authorizing state grants to match the Federal grants. Thirteen of the states had funded the matching program.

6. Water Pollution Control Act, sec. 8(c).

7. Information supplied to the author by the Bureau of the Budget.

8. Water Pollution Control Act, sec. 8(b).

9. See Comptroller General of the United States, "Examination into the Effectiveness of the Construction Grant Program for Abating, Controlling, and Preventing Water Pollution," November 3, 1969, pp. 22-40.

10. See Table 6-2.

11. Jeane Lowe, *Cities in a Race with Time* (New York: Random House, 1967), pp. 134-138.

12. See Table 4-4.

13. U.S. House of Representatives, Committee on Interstate and Foreign Commerce, "Hearings on S.780" (1967), p. 331.

14. *Ibid.*

15. Table 6-2.

16. "Progress in the Prevention and Control of Air Pollution," first report of the Secretary of HEW to the U.S. Congress, Senate Document 92 (90th Congress, 2nd session), June 28, 1968, p. 33. These figures do not square with Table 6-2 because of different interpretations of the data.

17. *Ibid.*, p. 34. Again there is some discrepancy between this figure and Table 6-2.

18. Letter from Dennis T. Karas, Director, Dept. of Air Quality Control, E. Chicago, Ind., to Sen. Birch Bayh, March 19, 1968, reprinted in U.S. Senate, "Air Pollution—1968," *op. cit.*, part 1, p. 254.

19. Lewis C. Green, chairman of the Missouri Air Conservation Commission, in U.S. Senate, "Air Pollution—1967," *op. cit.*, part 2, p. 997.

20. There are considerable economies of scale in the construction and operation of waste treatment plants. "Per capita investment for a sewage treatment plant to serve half a million people is 75% that of a facility serving 50,000. There are also considerable savings in per capita operating costs with large facilities. For example, it costs an average of $8.00 per million gallons to provide primary sewage treatment with a 100,000,000 gallon capacity treatment plant, for a 10,000,000 gallon capacity plant the comparable cost is $23.00. And costs are $58.00 for a 1,000,000 gallon capacity facility." Advisory Commission on Intergovernmental Relations, "Intergovernmental Responsibilities for Water Supply and Sewage Disposal in Metropolitan Areas" (Washington, D.C.: GPO, October 1962), p. 39.

21. *Ibid.*, Chaps. 3 and 4.

22. Matthew Holden, Jr., "Pollution Control as a Bargaining Process: An Essay on Regulatory Decision-Making" (Ithaca, N.Y.: Cornell University Water Resources Center, October 1966), p. 11.

23. *Ibid.*, pp. 42-43.

24. See Chapter 4, pp. 91 ff.

25. See Murphy, *Water Purity*, pp. 101-102.

26. See *New York Times,* October 19, 1969, 61:1.

27. See Holden, *op. cit.,* p. 37.

28. The Advisory Commission on Intergovernmental Relations (ACIR) has ranked fifteen governmental functions as to whether they can best be performed on a local or area-wide basis. Water supply and sewage disposal and air pollution control were rated as the "least local" functions. See ACIR, "Performance of Urban Functions: Local and Areawide" (Washington, D.C.: GPO, September 1963), pp. 8–23.

29. J. C. Bollens and H. J. Schmandt, *The Metropolis* (New York: Harper & Row, 1965), pp. 544–545.

30. See New England Interstate Water Pollution Control Compact, arts. IV and V.

31. For a full description of ORSANCO see Cleary, *op. cit.*

32. Richard A. Leach, "ORSANCO: A Twenty-Year Record," *State Government* (Winter 1968), pp. 49–56. Cleary denies that the provisions of the compact have hampered enforcement, but he also concedes that control of industrial pollution has not been totally satisfactory. See Cleary, *op. cit.,* pp. 214–217.

33. Leach, *op. cit.,* p. 54.

34. U.S. Senate, "Air Pollution—1968," *op. cit.,* part 1, p. 195.

35. For the background leading to the formation of the DRBC see R. C. Martin, *et al., River Basin Administration and the Delaware* (Syracuse, N.Y.: Syracuse University Press, 1960).

36. See FWPCA, "Delaware Estuary Comprehensive Study—Preliminary Report and Findings" (July 1966).

37. See Delaware River Basin Commission, "Annual Report—1968," pp. 6–7.

38. J. I. Bregman, "The Case for an Interstate Air Pollution Control Program," Paper E-4, National Conference on Air Pollution, Washington, D.C., December 13, 1966.

39. For a full discussion of all three compacts, see U.S. Senate, "Air Pollution—1968," *op. cit.,* part 1.

40. Sec. 102(c).

41. U.S. Senate, Committee on Public Works, "Recommendations of the Committee on Public Works to the Committee on the Judiciary Regarding the Conditional Consent of the Congress to Various Interstate Air Pollution Control Compacts" (1968).

42. "Progress in the Prevention and Control of Air Pollution," *op. cit.,* p. 34.

43. Remarks by Secretary of the Interior Stewart L. Udall at the annual meeting of the Delaware River Basin Commission, New York City, March 7, 1968.

44. U.S. Senate, "Air Pollution—1968," *op. cit.,* part 1, p. 461.

45. See Morton Grodzins, *The Federal System* (Chicago: Rand McNally, 1966).

46. Frank Graham, Jr., *Disaster by Default: Politics and Water Pollution* (New York: M. Evans, 1966), pp. 100–101.

CHAPTER 7

1. This is a good illustration of Weinberg's thesis that technological solutions are easier than political solutions. See Alvin Weinberg, "Can Technology Replace Social Engineering?", *Bulletin of the Atomic Scientists* XXII:10 (December 1966), pp. 4–8.

2. See U.S. Dept. of Commerce, Panel on Electrically Powered Vehicles, "The Automobile and Air Pollution: A Program for Progress" (Washington, D.C.: GPO, October 1967).

3. "Background Material for the Development of Radiation Protection Standards," staff report of the Federal Radiation Council, May 13, 1960, reprinted May 1965 by HEW, p. 24. For a cogent argument along the same lines see Barry Commoner, *Science and Survival* (New York: Viking, 1967), pp. 90–102.

4. To translate this emission standard into a limitation on the sulfur content of coal, it is only necessary to know that 1 pound of sulfur will produce 2 pounds of sulfur dioxide and that an average pound of coal contains 13,000 BTU. By multiplying the emission standard times 13,000 and then dividing by 2, one can translate the limit of 0.34 pounds of sulfur dioxide per million BTU into a limitation of 0.2 per cent on the sulfur content of coal.

5. HEW, Office of the Assistant Secretary for Planning and Evaluation, "An Economic Analysis of the Control of Sulphur Oxides Air Pollution" (December 1967), p. V–1.

6. Despite its source, the best guide to the intricacies of the Air Quality Act is "A Guide to the Air Quality Act of 1967" (Washington, D.C.: The National Coal Policy Conference, Inc., n.d.).

7. See Table 7–1.

8. Sec. 108(c)(1).

9. Clean Air Act, sec. 103(c)(2).

10. *Ibid.,* sec. 103(c)(3).

11. Water Pollution Control Act, as amended, sec. 10(c)(1). See also Murphy, *Governing Nature,* pp. 239–240, and Cleary, *op. cit.,* p. 151 and p. 266.

12. HEW, Public Health Service, "Air Quality Criteria for Sulfur Oxides" (Washington, D.C.: GPO, March 1967).

13. *Ibid.,* p. vi.

14. U.S. Senate, Committee on Public Works, Subcommittee on Air and Water Pollution, "Air Quality Criteria" (July 1968), p. 14.

15. Sec. 107(b)(1).

16. U.S. Senate, "Air Pollution—1967," *op. cit.,* part 3, p. 1154.

17. Air Quality Act, sec. 107(b)(1).

18. HEW, Public Health Service, "Air Quality Criteria for Sulfur Oxides" (Washington, D.C.: GPO, January 1969), pp. 10–22.

19. National Coal Policy Conference Newsletter, February 13, 1969, p. 1.

20. Although the new version was issued in February, it retained the January date on the cover, thus making it indistinguishable from the first version except for a notation indicating that a new final page had been substituted.

21. U.S. Senate, "Air Pollution—1968," *op. cit.,* part 1, p. 252.

22. Another factor forcing HEW to reach a decision on a sulfur oxides standard was the department's intervention in Federal Power Commission cases involving the allocation of additional natural gas for Los Angeles, New York, and Florida. HEW argued that the FPC should allocate additional natural gas to these locations because of the danger of sulfur oxides air pollution. In its testimony before the FPC, HEW was forced to estimate what the desirable level of sulfur oxides should be.

23. The letter was made part of the committee report on the Clean Air Act amendments. See U.S. House of Representatives, Committee on Interstate and Foreign Commerce, "Report on Clean Air and Solid Waste Acts," Report 899 (89th Congress, 1st session), August 31, 1965, p. 3.

24. See Code of Federal Regulations, Title 42, subchapter F, sec. 76.5(A), for the HEW regulations implementing the Executive Order.

25. Statement of National Coal Policy Conference, National Coal Association, and United Mine Workers of America presented to HEW, January 20, 1967: "Proposed Regulations of Sulfur Oxides Emissions by Federal Installations in New York, Chicago, and Philadelphia Metropolitan Areas."

26. In 1968, Congress denied a request for funds by the Office of Science and Technology to form a modest staff to provide such a study. OST is, however, going ahead and trying to assemble some of the necessary data to form a basis for a national energy policy.

27. The letter appears in *Presidential Documents,* 3:16 (April 24, 1967), pp. 651–652.

28. U.S. Department of Commerce, *Statistical Abstract of the United States, 1968,* Table 1025; and information supplied by U.S. Dept. of the Interior, Bureau of Mines.

29. U.S. Senate, "Water Pollution—1967," *op. cit.,* part 2, p. 502.

30. *Ibid.,* p. 507.

31. *Ibid.,* p. 551.

32. *Ibid.,* p. 609.

33. See Remarks by Max N. Edwards, Assistant Secretary of the Interior for Water Pollution Control, at the meeting of the Missouri Basin Inter-Agency Committee, Grand Teton National Park, Wyoming, June 27, 1968, p. 3.

34. See Luther J. Carter, "Water Pollution: Officials Goaded into Raising Quality Standards," *Science,* April 5, 1968.

35. Dept. of the Interior news release, February 8, 1968.

36. *New York Times,* May 15, 1968, 29:2.

37. *New York Times,* May 8, 1968, 16:1.

38. Remarks by Max N. Edwards, June 27, 1968, *op. cit.,* p. 10.

39. FWPCA, "Guidelines for Establishing Water Quality Standards for Interstate Waters" (May 1966), p. 7.

40. Remarks before the National Association of Manufacturers, New York, N.Y., October 31, 1968, p. 5. See also Mitchell Wendell, "Intergovernmental Relations in Water Quality Control," *Journal of the Water Pollution Control Federation,* 39:2 (February 1967), pp. 278–284.

41. U.S. Senate, "Water Pollution—1967," *op. cit.,* part 2, p. 609.

42. *Ibid.,* p. 624.

43. *Ibid.,* p. 501.

CHAPTER 8

1. See Allen Kneese and Blair Bower, *Managing Water Quality: Economics, Technology, Institutions* (Baltimore: Johns Hopkins Press, 1968), Chaps. 6–8. For a variation of the effluent fee proposal, see Dales, *Pollution, Property and Prices,* Chap. 6.

2. In the economist's language, effluent fees would achieve the "Pareto optimal solution" in a watershed. See Kneese and Bower, *op. cit.*

3. See Otto A. Davis and Morton I. Kamien, "Externalities, Information and Alternative Collective Action," in U.S. Congress, Joint Economic Committee, "The Analysis and Evaluation of Public Expenditures," *op. cit.,* Vol. 1, pp. 67–86.

4. For a simplified model which incorporates both economic criteria and political influence, see Robert Dorfman and Henry Jacoby, "A Model of Public Decisions Illustrated by a Water Pollution Policy Problem," in "The Analysis and Evaluation of Public Expenditures," *op. cit.,* Vol. 1, pp. 226–274.

5. For a favorable estimate of the Genossenschaften, see Kneese and Bower, *op. cit.,* Chaps. 12 and 13.

6. For other criticisms of effluent fees from the viewpoint of an economist, see Harold Wolozin, "The Economics of Air Pollution: Central Problems," in *Law and Contemporary Problems,* XXXIII:2 (Spring 1968), pp. 227–238.

7. Water Pollution Control Act, sec. 10(d)(1).

8. Clean Air Act, sec. 108(k)

9. *New York Times,* September 4, 1969, 1:4.

10. U.S. Senate, "Water Pollution—1967," *op. cit.,* part 2, p. 676.

11. Letter from John E. Daniel, staff assistant for Standards and Compliance, NAPCA, to the author, July 15, 1969.

12. Sec. 103(e).

13. The Nixon order is dated February 4, 1970. The Johnson orders were E.O. 11288 (water pollution) and E.O. 11282 (air pollution).

14. U.S. Senate, Committee on Public Works, "Amending the Federal Water Pollution Control Act, As Amended, and for Other Purposes," Report 91-351 (91st Congress, 1st session), August 7, 1969, pp. 7–8.

15. *New York Times,* October 19, 1969, 61:1.

16. Clean Air Act, sec. 101(3), and Water Pollution Control Act, sec. 1(6).

17. Cleary, *op. cit.,* p. 261.

18. This was indirectly confirmed when Carl L. Klein, the Nixon Administration's Assistant Secretary for Water Quality, told *New York Times* reporter Gladwin Hill that the new administration would rely on informal negotiations rather than formal conferences. "My idea is to just talk problem situations out with officials in the states. I think we can get action that way, cutting through the red tape without all these cumbersome formal proceedings," said Klein. After a strongly adverse reaction from the mass media, conservationists, and the members of the Water Pollution Control Advisory Board, Klein withdrew his statement. See Gladwin Hill, "U.S. Shifts Fight on Dirty Water," *New York Times* May 18, 1969, 44:1, and William Blair, "U.S. to Continue Water Hearings," *New York Times,* May 29, 1969, 22:6.

19. HEW, "Summary of Conference and Conclusions and Recommendations on Interstate Air Pollution New York-New Jersey Metropolitan Area," January 1967, p. 2.

20. See Sigurd Grava, *Urban Planning Aspects of Water Pollution Control* (New York: Columbia University Press, 1969); and C. Peter Rydell and Gretchen Schwarz, "Air Pollution and Urban Form: A Review of Current Literature," *Journal of the American Institute of Planners,* XXXIV:2 (March 1968), pp. 115–120.

21. HEW, "An Economic Analysis of the Control of Sulphur Oxides Air Pollution," *op. cit.,* p. III–13.

CHAPTER 9

1. *New York Times,* October 19, 1969, 61:1.

2. See Reorganization Plan No. 2 of 1966, secs. 1(c) and (f).

3. See Kneese and Bower, *op. cit.,* pp. 125–129.

4. M. Mason Gaffney, "Welfare Economics and the Environment," in Henry Jarrett, ed., *Environmental Quality in a Growing Economy* (Baltimore: Johns Hopkins Press, 1966), p. 101. See also Aaron Wildavsky, "Aesthetic Power or the Triumph of the Sensitive Minority Over the Vulgar Mass: A Political Analysis of the New Economics," *Daedalus,* 96:4 (Fall 1967), pp. 1115–1128.

5. See U.S. Senate, Committee on Public Works, "Air Quality Criteria" (July 1968), p. 55.

6. In 1966 a Division of Environmental Health Sciences (later renamed the National Institute of Environmental Health Sciences) was

formed as part of the National Institutes of Health within HEW. The agency defines its mission as: "First, to determine the magnitude and significance of the hazard to man's health inherent in long-term exposures to low-level concentrations of biological, chemical, and physical environmental agents; second, to identify the underlying mechanisms of adverse response with the hope that principles related to this response can be established as a scientific base for criteria on which to set standards and to provide predictive guides to be used by control agencies for protective or preventive measures"— HEW, Public Health Service, National Institutes of Health, "Environmental Health Sciences" (1969), p. 7. As of January 1, 1969, the Institute had employed only forty-eight scientists, and there are indications that its primary emphasis will be on basic health research rather than on gathering the information necessary for setting specific standards. Furthermore, it is not making any attempt systematically to monitor or examine the large number of pollutants present in the environment.

7. Registration of new chemicals and trace metals has been recommended by the HEW Task Force on Environmental Health and Related Problems. See "A Strategy for a Livable Environment" (Washington, D.C.: GPO, 1967), p. 20. Monitoring of such substances in the environment was explored several years ago by PHS and was determined feasible.

8. It has been estimated that half of the total volume of wastes processed by municipal plants is of industrial origin. See letter of January 16, 1969, from the Secretary of the Interior transmitting to Congress a summary of conclusions from "The Cost of Clean Water."

9. We have already discussed the disadvantages of tax incentives. However, many of these disadvantages might be overcome if the legislation were drawn up with sufficient imagination. For example, Paul Gerhardt has suggested that an incentive could be designed to cover operating as well as capital costs and that tax credits "might be limited to the extent that annualized pollution control costs exceed some share (say one per cent) of value added on a plant basis." These two recommendations would overcome the distortions produced by only giving money for end-of-the-line capital investments and would prevent the subsidy from going to those firms that need it least. See Paul H. Gerhardt, "Can Governments Buy Air Pollution Control?", paper presented at the annual meeting of the Association of American Geographers, Washington, D.C., August 22, 1968, p. 9.

10. U.S. Senate, "Air Pollution—1967," *op. cit.,* part 2, p. 847.

11. *New York Times,* June 24, 1969, 4:3.

Index

Acid mine drainage, 29, 46, 49
Advertising Council, 173
Aesthetics, 20, 196-7
Agencies: conflicts among, 115-119, 149; coordination of, 100-103, 116-119; Federal, 23, 98-103, 108-116; interstate, 134-141, 174, 190; local, 51, 83-84; power of, 18, 23, 116-117; state, 51, 83-84; *See also* names of
Agriculture, 24, 26-31, 96, 107, 115, 196
Agriculture Committee, 66
Air: natural state of, 19; quality standards for, 55, 153, 157
Air Conservation Commission, 89
Air pollution: by automobiles, 33, 53, 66, 95, 126, 204; by chemicals, 147; congressional investigations of, 70-73, 109
 control of: agencies for, 23, 51, 83-84, 98-108, 115-119, 135-141, 149; benefits of, 148, 196-197; conservation groups and, 84-90; costs of, 19, 21, 148; enforcement of, 113, 157, 180-191; equipment for, 89, 91-92, 95, 178; Federal government and, 17-18, 21, 29, 33-58, 61-76, 91, 98-103, 105, 107, 142, 157, 164, 168-170, 175, 180-187, 190, 200, 203-205; funds for, 17-18, 21, 73, 84, 105-107, 112, 113, 117, 129, 148-150, 157, 167, 184, 200; international, 142, 204-5; interstate, 51, 134-141, 174, 190; legislation for, 29,33,35-58,61-76,91,104-105,200; local government and, 38, 57, 83-84, 104-105, 120-144; objectives of, 156; planning for, 113, 129, 191-192; regulations for, 35, 106, 107; responsibility for, 125-130; standards of, 18, 19, 157-163; state government and, 51, 83-84, 120-144; tax relief and, 93; techniques

of, 148-150; violators of, 132-134
 control regions, 157
 defined, 33-36
 economy and, 106
 health and, 34, 88, 196
 by incinerators, 33
 industry and, 90-97, 151-152, 168
 natural, 19
 public opinion on, 21-24, 77-97
 radioactivity, 29, 34, 66, 99, 154, 198
 research on, 53, 55, 57, 70-71, 106-108, 112, 113, 148, 151
 science and, 89, 149
 water pollution compared to, 35-36, 194-196
Air Pollution Control Association, 89-90
Air Quality Act, 50, 54, 57, 64, 94-95, 106, 129, 138-140, 142, 157-158, 160, 167, 169, 175, 181, 191, 192, 203-204
Air sheds, 134, 177, 196
Algae, 19, 32
American Academy for the Advancement of Science, 89
American Federation of Labor-Congress Industrial Organization (AFL-CIO), 87
American Machine and Foundry, 95
American Medical Association (AMA), 89
Animals, 27-28, 160, 201
Anti-degradation, 171-173
Appalachian Regional Development Act, 114
Appropriations, 73-76
Association of Attorneys' General, 172
Association of State and Territorial Health Officers, 88
Atomic Energy Commission (AEC), 47, 99

DATE DUE